BOUTIQUE LODGINGS
of New Zealand

7th
EDITION

PERSONALLY REVIEWED AND NARRATED
BOUTIQUE HOTELS, INNS, BED & BREAKFASTS,
URAL RETREATS, LODGES AND SELF-CONTAINED
COTTAGES THROUGHOUT NEW ZEALAND.

Boutique Lodgings of New Zealand
7th edition

ISBN Print 978-0-473-12540-0
      Web 978-0-473-12541-7

Published by   ~
The Formula (Publications) Ltd
PO Box 911070
Auckland Mail Centre
Auckland
New Zealand
www.lodgings.co.nz
editor@lodgings.co.nz

Design and typesetting
Meadowset Graphics Ltd, Auckland

Printing
Geon Group

Cover Photographs: Front Cover – **Grasmere Lodge**, Cass,
Canterbury
Back Cover - Clockwise left to right:
Hapuku Lodge - Kaikoura, **Corstorphine House** - Dunedin,
Old Saint Mary's Convent Retreat - Blenheim,
Matuka Lodge - Twizel, **Pukeko Landing** - Lake Tarawera.
Centre: **Rippinvale Retreat** - Hanmer Springs.
Photography: Tim Findley, members of Boutique Lodgings.

Contact Details;
The Formula(Publications) Ltd
P.O Box 911070 AMSC
Auckland
Ph + 649 3691113
Fax +649 5295623
Editor: Jenny Nagel

As from 1st December 2006 Boutique Lodgings of New Zealand is being published by The Formula (Publications) Ltd under the directorship of Jenny Nagel who has had many years experience in sales and marketing.

The new team has much pleasure in presenting this 7th edition. All Boutique Lodgings properties have been selected for their superior facilities, spectacular locations, warm hospitality, character and ambience. All have been personally sought out and experienced by a member of our team with the aim of giving you the most accurate impression for you to choose if a property is right for you as we recognize everyone's experience and tastes are different. For this the 7th edition all properties carry the official New Zealand Tourism's Qualmark quality mark to help international and domestic travelers select places to stay, things to do and ways to get around. (see inside back cover for more details). All Boutique Lodgings members have also been selected for their ongoing commitment to sustainable tourism and business practices.

We proudly present to you this comprehensive up to date guide to superb accommodation in a user friendly conveniently sized publication which stands beside our established and active website. www.lodgings.co.nz

New Zealand is unique in many ways. From subtropical Northland to the snow capped mountains of the south, the visitor can enjoy a world in miniature without the necessity to travel vast distances. Whatever your interests, be it game fishing, trout fishing, whale watching in Kaikoura, alpine sports, the fascinating geothermal activities in the Central North Island, a round or two of golf on one of the many courses for which New Zealand is noted or just relaxation in luxurious and picturesque surroundings, there is a member of Boutique Lodgings nearby to welcome you. Many of these guest houses are of historical significance and have been lovingly refurbished to their former glory. Others are purpose built but all offer the discerning visitor some memorable aspects of New Zealand.

A special thanks to Boutique Lodgings hosts who made our research possible and enjoyable.

Thanks also go to all who have contributed to this publication, Tim and Elaine who traveled the country visiting members and providing wonderful photography, Barbara for taking care of the office and the systems and Veronica for ensuring that when we needed information it was in the right place. Without them this publication would not have been possible.

All photographs used in this publication have been supplied either by our members' or by members' of our team.

We welcome you to a taste of New Zealand, and hope that this publication has inspired you to visit this wonderful country and enjoy the superb hospitality and level of accommodation that our members' provide.

Feed back is crucial to ensuring that future editions of Boutique Lodgings of New Zealand fulfill the requirements of you, the user of the publication, please visit our website or email us with your views. Any suggestions as to how it may be improved or what additional information would be helpful to you would be most welcome. Should you wish to obtain any advice on were to go and what to see whist planning your holiday do not hesitate to contact us as we are happy to assist.

Jenny Nagel

editor@lodgings.co.nz
www.lodgings.co.nz

Table of contents   Pages

Colour Coded Regions/Maps

Each of the nine regions has been colour coded as
shown on the map opposite. Colour coded maps listing
cities and towns with respective property page numbers
can be found at the beginning of each section.

Using this Guide

Boutique Lodgings of New Zealand aims to be as user friendly as possible. We welcome any suggestions for improvement for future editions.

All accommodation must be booked in advance unless otherwise stated. Cancellation policies are applied as part of the properties Qualmark process and will vary. Boutique Lodgings of New Zealand do not charge any of our members' commission for bookings made through this publication or our website.

Cover Flaps

The back and front cover flaps contain important information pertaining to using the book. The flaps also double as bookmarks to help with your travel planning.

Areas / Maps

The properties are divided into 9 regions that generally follow a set travelling route. Properties are listed north to south where possible. On the inside of the front and back covers we have included North and South Island maps and distance charts to help you in your itinerary planning. We suggest a good touring map to be used in conjunction with the book as our maps show only main travelling routes.

Custom Tours

You will also find information on our recommended travel guide whether you choose to be guided or travel independently

Check in / Check out Times (approx.)

Check-in: mid - late afternoon
Check-out: between 10am and 11am.
Please check with your host at the time of booking.

Property Pages

Contact a Property

Each property page lists the property's address and phone number. Here, you will also find the property's Boutique Lodgings of New Zealand website address. From this online page you can send an inquiry form straight through to your selected property and/or view further information about them.

Property Features

Activities listed and tea/coffee are generally included in the tariff, please enquire when booking.

Local Features

These include features in the surrounding area specific to the property. The features are personally highlighted by property owners themselves.

Travel Times

All travel times are by motor vehicle unless otherwise stated. This is an indication only and will depend on the driver and road conditions.

Tariff Chart

Tariffs are correct at the time of printing and all prices are in New Zealand dollars and include GST (tax), so please check rates when you book. If applicable please ask about long term and off-season rates.

 1 person occupancy   2 person occupancy

 Extra person if there are facilities to sleep more than 2 people

Property Pages (cont).

Bed Sizes
S	Single bed
D	Double bed
Q	Queen bed
K	King bed
SK	Super-king bed
CK	Californian-king bed
SK/T	Super-king that splits into 2 singles for twin occupancy

Bathroom Types
EN - Ensuites: exclusive use inside guestroom.
PR - Private: exclusive use outside bedroom
GS - Guest Shared: share with other guests

Helpful Advice:
Using the Telephone:
In emergency.............**dial 111**
To call from NZ, dial our international access code (00), the country code eg. United States (1), followed by your area code eg. California (619), then the 7-digit telephone number. For example 00 1 619 1234 567.

Conversions
Conversion to imperial	Conversion to metric
1 kph = 0.621 mph	1 mph = 1.61 kph
1 litre = 0.26 US gallons	1 US gallon = 3.79 litres
or 0.22 UK gallons	1 UK gallon = 4.55 litres
1 hectare = 2.471 acres	1 acre = 0.4045 hectares

Public Holidays
New Zealand has 8 national public holidays.
New Year	1-2 January
Waitangi Day	6 February
Easter (varies)	March/April
Anzac Day	25 April
Queen's Birthday (varies)	June
Labour Day (varies)	October
Christmas Day	25 December
Boxing Day	26 December

Regional Holidays
New Zealand also has anniversary days for each of its regions. These are only celebrated within the region and usually fall on the nearest Monday to the dates below:

Southland	17 January
Wellington	22 January
Auckland	29 January
Northland	29 January
Nelson	1 February
Otago	23 March
Taranaki	31 March
South Canterbury	25 September
Hawkes Bay	1 November
Marlborough	1 November
Westland	1 December
Canterbury	16 December

Kiwi words to learn...
Aubergine	eggplant
Bach	small holiday home (North Island)
Biscuit	cookie
Bonnet	car hood
Boot	car trunk
Brekkie	breakfast
Bum-bag	fanny pack
BYO	Bring Your Own (usually wine or beer)
Capsicum	bell pepper
Cellotape	scotch tape
Courgette	zucchini
Cheers	goodbye, thank you
Chemist	pharmacy
Chilli bin	cooler/eskie
Chips	French fries/crisps/potato chips
Crib	small holiday home (South Island)
Crook	be sick, ill
Dairy	a convenience store or corner shop
Dunny	toilet
Entrée	appetizer or hors d'oeuvre
Flannel	wash cloth
Flat white	a short espresso with hot steamed milk
Fortnight	fourteen days, two weeks
Holiday	vacation
Ice block	popsicle
Jersey	sweater
Kia ora	Maori for hello
Kumara	sweet potato
Lemonade	7up
Licensed	can legally sell alcoholic beverages
Lift	elevator
Lolly	candy/sweet
Loo	bathroom
Motorway	freeway
Maori	indigenous people of NZ
Mossie	mosquito
Pakeha	a non-Maori New Zealander
Spa pool	jacuzzi
S/C	self-contained – has a kitchen(ette)
Sweet as	great, fine
Tiki tour	roundabout way to get somewhere
Tomato sauce	catsup/ketchup
Tramping	hiking
Torch	flashlight
Vegemite/Marmite	breakfast spreads (kiwi favourites)

Tailored Travel
New Zealand Custom Tours

Personal Guided Custom Tours
Throughout New Zealand

Imagine having a guide with an intimate knowledge of New Zealand who can bring together the best suited accommodation for your privately escorted luxury custom tour.

Your trip will be completely planned and arranged with my extensive expertise and experience, creating a careful balance of culture, scenery and people. YOUR specific interests and input will make it truly unique and personal, whether you chose to be guided or travel independently.

Your exclusive custom tour will encompass your individual interests from wine and cuisine to short nature walks and Maori cultural events.

For you to know New Zealand rather than just see it, I limit each exclusive guided tour to four people.

Savoring gourmet meals of fresh local produce and wine, relaxing in the luxury of boutique lodgings - everything you see and do will be at your pace and leisure on your escorted private tour.

Save time wading through a myriad of information and choose a proven and trusted guided custom tour, delivered by a New Zealand based company operating since 1990.

I invite you to join me on your unique, personal New Zealand tour experience which is inimitable.

Go to www.newzealandcustomtours.com/actionnow.asp to start planning.

Ka Kite Ano (until we meet)

Robert

Robert Panzer

www.NewZealandCustomTours.com

"We recently returned from a fabulous trip to New Zealand. I wanted to pass on the name of our guide as he was the best we have ever had in all of our travels. His name is Robert Panzer of Tailored Travel. After we filled out a questionnaire as to our interests, he planned a custom tour for us - he made reservations at five star B&Bs, did all the driving, took us to all the best restaurants, and took all the worry out of travelling. It was a "no headache" trip."

Ralph and Allyn, USA

qualmark
endorsed
visitor activity

Tailored Travel
New Zealand Custom Tours
Thorpe, Nelson
New Zealand
Ph: +64 3 543 3825
Fax: +64 3 543 3640
Robert@customtours.co.nz

THE ROAD TO DISCOVERY

To discover the true heart of New Zealand the best way to travel is by road. The New Zealand scenery is spectacular. It's a land of diversity, from snow capped mountains and volcanoes, rugged coastlines, lakes, lush bush, farmed pasture and much more. However this country is not all about scenery. Make sure that you take the time to get to know it, as New Zealand is really about the people. You will find warm, friendly, generous hosts who are well traveled and willing to provide exceptional levels of hospitality. However be warned, time is a precious thing and to see all there is to see and do in New Zealand requires lots of it. Browse through our publication and plan according to your interests, the need for a relaxing holiday and comfortable traveling times. The roads are in most cases two laned highways and often twist around spectacular coastlines, over hills and through valleys and require care. Every region has its story to tell and it own particular charm.

Below we have offered some suggestions based on the various regions in this publication:

NORTH ISLAND

Northland "The Winterless North"
Auckland is your starting point to travel north through the giant Kauri forests, to the famed Ninety Mile Beach. Then head back around the eastern coast for spectacular golden sand beaches, legendry game fishing and some of the best golf courses in the world. The Warkworth region is a burgeoning wine and arts district. To see Northland would take a week at least.

Auckland "The Beautiful City of Sails"
A wonderful start to your New Zealand experience with a magnificent harbour, for exciting nightlife try the viaduct, visit wild west coast beaches and for the shoppers a visit to Newmarket, Remuera or Ponsonby has to be on the agenda. The Museum is also renowned and a great place to get a feel of the history of this great country.

West North Island "The Adventure Coast"
Take in the stud farms of Cambridge then travel west for legendary surfing, Waitomo caves, the Tongario Crossing, and Taranaki for some of the most spectacular farming and garden scenery in the world.

Central Plateau "The Cultural Experience"
Rotorua is acclaimed for its heritage and famous Geysers, and visit beautiful Taupo for a spot of trout fishing. Base yourself here for a visit to the mountains to try the ski slopes.

East North Island "The Great Kiwi Summer Holiday"
Travel east to the spectacular beaches of the Coromandel Peninsula, where Cathedral Cove and Hot Water Beach are highlights. The Bay of Plenty is a fruit bowl of choice, while the vast area from Gisborne through Hawkes Bay to Martinborough is renowned for wine growing. This area is a growing tourist destination and would take several days to even skim it.

SOUTH ISLAND

Nelson Marlborough "The Outdoor Adventure"
This area is vast, from Abel Tasman National Park to Kaikoura and there is much to see and do. Try tramping and kayaking the National Park. Tour the vineyards of Blenheim and whale watch in Kaikoura. A week is never long enough.

West Coast "The Scenic Holiday"
The coast is a must do for scenery and outdoor sports, from the start of the famed Heaphy track down to Haast you will travel long and winding roads, but you will be rewarded. Stop at all the towns on the way, they offer a truly unique level of kiwi hospitality. Visit the Glaciers and the 'Pancake Rocks' and fish the streams. Take your time.

Canterbury "The Sophisticated Holiday"
This area is diverse, from the springs at Hanmer to the art centres of Christchurch and Akaroa, out across the plains towards Arthur's Pass it's a land of change. Fishing and tramping are excellent. Take in the lakes at Tekapo and South Canterbury is the ideal spot for a game of golf.

Otago "The Deep South"
From the heritage areas of Oamaru in North Otago and Dunedin head around the coast to the Catlins or head inland to the tourist destinations of Wanaka and Queenstown. For the thrill seekers the choice is enormous skiing, water sports, and hang gliding. For beautiful scenery it is a must. Visit the Fiords at Te Anau and then for the ultimate outdoor adventure head to Stewart Island and take a visit to the nature reserve of Ulva Island. You may never leave.

We have given a brief overview of our country, and there is so much more. New Zealand has without a doubt some of the world's best getaway accommodation, if it's pampering you require, complete privacy in tranquil surroundings or an outdoor adventure to tell the kids about in years to come, it's all here.

We are happy to help you plan your vacation or better still have our recommended **travel planner** do everything for you. Just sit back and enjoy the experience, we guarantee that you will not be disappointed.

So never forget we are just guardians of this great land.

Coopers Beach Mangonui page 14
page 13   Whangaroa page 15
Ahipara   Te Ngaere Bay page 17
page 12   Kerikeri page 18

Ohaeawai   Bay of Islands page 25
page 24
Waipoua Forest
(Kauri Coast)
page 31   Whangarei page 27

Russell - Bay of Islands

Courtesy of Flagstaff Lodge

11

Shipwreck Lodge

Roger and Laura Raduenz
70 Foreshore Road, Ahipara, Northland
Tel: 09 4094929
Fax: 09 4094928
shipwrecklodge@xtra.co.nz
www.lodgings.co.nz – keyword: shipwrecklodge

Property features
Luxurious/contemporary home
Unlimited views of 90 mile beach
Brilliant westward sunsets
Private balconies overlooking sea
Local features
90 Mile beach
Golf course
Swimming/surfing/fishing
Adventure activities
Cape Reinga 1.5 hour drive

Ahipara - 3 mins walk
Kaitaia - 14 mins drive

From south of Kaitaia take left turn to Ahipara. From north of Kaitaia tur right to Ahipara. 14 kilometres to Ahipara turn left at school. The lodg• is 600 metres on your right.

This purpose built, modern lodge is situated at Shipwreck Bay from which it takes its name. It is only a few metres from the dun-coloured sands of Ninety Mile Beach where the white frilled edges of the sea roll relentlessly onto the land. I slept upstairs in one of the three guestrooms each opening to private balconies and affording views of the great arc of coastline stretching north to Cape Reinga. The rooms are spacious, uncluttered and fitted with convenient and attractive furnishings and restful décor. There's also a small guest lounge at the top of the stairs, which has a fridge and tea-and-coffee-making facilities. The lower floor has been designed for relaxed living with tiled floors, high studs and wide fold-out doors opening to a small lawn and the beach beyond. To one side of the communal open-plan kitchen/dining room/lounge is a smaller lounge with Sky television for guest's use and this also leads to a small courtyard. The beach is only a short walk away over sand dunes carpeted by natural foliage. In the evening I watched a blazing sunset that often lights the sky in this part of the world and by day I enjoyed the fishing, swimming or touring that the area offers.

Accommodation available (NZ$)	♦	♦♦	+♦	⊂⟩	⌐	
1 Room			$200-250	Q	EN	Breakfast: Cooked
1 Room			$250-300	K	EN	Evening meal: $70pp
1 Suite			$300-350	K or 2S	EN	Guest rooms:
						Ambience:
						Setting/location:

Evening meal by prior arrangement.

LOW   HIGH

Property features
Kayaks/gym
50 channel cable TV
Beachfront location
Host speaks German
Boogie boards
Local features
Quaint fishing village
Golden sandy beaches
Deep sea and fishing charters
Golf course
Cape Reinga day trips

Beach Lodge
Margaret Morrison
121 State Highway 10, Coopers Beach
Tel: 09 4060068
Fax: 09 4060068
margaret@beachlodge.co.nz
www.lodgings.co.nz – keyword: beachlodge

Mangonui - 5 mins drive
Kaitaia - 30 mins drive

Approximately 30 minutes north of Kaeo on SH10 take the Mangonui by-pass. Continue 3km to Coopers Beach. Beach Lodge is on your right (ocean side).

    The view from the deck defies description. Because the five self-contained units are elevated just above beautiful Coopers Beach, the outlook from two units is unobstructed across Doubtless Bay. The other units have fabulous sea views through the impressive Pohutukawa trees. The two bedroom units are independent and tastefully furnished, each with its own deck leading off the lounge and lower bedroom. The main feature of Beach Lodge is its magnificent location, yet the facilities deserve a special mention. My unit, as all the others, had a full kitchen complete with large fridge/freezer, microwave, under-bench oven, hob and quality crockery and glasses. Some nights I preferred to eat at my favourite fish-and-chip shop, five minutes away in Mangonui. In the units are thoughtful extras such as herbal heatpacks for tired drivers and complimentary packets of fudge. I was there in summer and I lazed on the deck, enjoying a G&T with Margaret who is a fabulous host. In winter it would be great to cocoon myself in this self-indulgent luxury in front of the 50-channel cable television. I found Beach Lodge the perfect place to relax. At night, I was lulled to sleep by the sound of lapping water just a few meters away.

Accommodation available (NZ$)	👤	👥	+👤	🛏	🛁
5 S/C units			$250-500	$30	Q+2S	PR

Breakfast: Not available

Guest rooms:
Ambience:
Setting/location:

LOW   HIGH

Peak season rates (extra $20) apply 1 Dec - 31 May. All apartments have wireless connection.

13

Carneval Ocean View

Roly and Martha Fasnacht
360 State Highway 10, Cable Bay, Mangonui 0420
Tel: 09 4061012
Fax: 09 4061012
fasnacht@xtra.co.nz
www.lodgings.co.nz – keyword: carneval

(P) 🚶 ✉ 📺

Property features
Panoramic seaview
Sauna
Wind surfboard/kayak
Terrace with stunning view
TV/VCR/40 programs
German/French/Swiss spoken
Local features
Safe beaches
Boating/fishing/ diving
Historic village Mangonui
Cape Reinga trips etc. organised

Mangonui - 5 mins drive
KeriKeri - 45 mins/Kaitaia - 30 mins drive

From the turn off to Mangonui, follow
SH 10 to Coopers Beach. Continue
to Cable Bay. Cross bridge and
opposite the rest area turn left up
driveway.

High above Doubtless Bay guests at Carneval Ocean View enjoy the sight of scalloped pink-sand beaches, glittering sea and shadowy headlands. Tables and chairs have been set around the outside of the house to maximise the view whatever the weather. There are two cheerfully furnished guest bedrooms. Mine had a wonderful view through a large picture window; the other has a similar outlook from its adjoining conservatory. Both rooms have large walk-in wardrobes, ensuite bathrooms, televisions, videos and tea and coffee-making facilities, but I was also encouraged to share the other areas of this peaceful and comfortably appointed house. Martha says many people come here as guests and leave as friends. She and Roly came to New Zealand eight years ago and speak several languages. Their Swiss name translates as Carneval in English. Roly is a qualified chef and if pre-arranged will cook dinner for his guests. But there are also many excellent restaurants close by which includes the country's best fish and chip shop. Roly served me his Swiss-style breakfast on the sheltered terrace overlooking Cable Bay. Down the hill I enjoyed the safe swimming beaches using the snorkelling gear and a surfboard that are for guests use.

Accommodation available (NZ$)			+		🛁
2 Suites	$150-190	$35	K	EN	

Breakfast: Special cooked
Evening meal: $45pp
Guest rooms:
Ambience:
Setting/location:

LOW   HIGH

Property features
Panoramic harbour views
Heated swimming pool
Spa pool
DVD library & CD player
TV 5 channels incl. sky sport
Local features
Golf courses - 20 mins
Harbour cruises & sailing charters
Big game fishing & diving
Eco walks & kauri forests
Trout fishing

Kerikeri - 30 mins drive
Paihia - 45 mins drive

Tauranga Bay
WAIMANU LODGE
Cavalli Islands
Matauri Bay
Kaeo
Kerikeri

From Kerikeri travel 25 kms north on SH 10 towards Kaeo. 3 kms after Kaeo turn right (at the one way bridge). Continue for 9 kms until you reach Whangaroa Harbour. Continue pass the game fishing club to the next turn on the right, Old Hospital Rd, to the top

Waimanu Lodge

Shaun and Judy Ledward
76 Old Hospital Road, Whangaroa Harbour, Northland
Tel: 09 4051340
Fax: 09 4051341
waimanulodge@xtra.co.nz
www.lodgings.co.nz – keyword: waimanulodge

Travel north to the world renowned Whangaroa Harbour, past the Hotel and the Game Fishing Club and there at the top of the hill you will find Waimanu Lodge. Step back, take a breath and just absorb the panoramic view spread out before you. Waimanu Lodge catering for couples has two beautifully appointed units. Both are spacious with every need catered for and flow out on to the deck surrounding the heated swimming pool and private spa pool. Overlooking the harbour I found this was the perfect place to unwind, take a book, a glass of wine and just enjoy the splendour of the surroundings. Shaun and Judy are wonderful hosts and if taking time out is not on your agenda then they are happy to arrange numerous activities. Waimanu Lodge is an ideal place to stay a few days. There is game fishing, sailing, golfing - several courses within 30 minutes drive – and if you really must experience a more incredible view then St Paul's Rock is right at your doorstep. Judy is passionate about food and a gourmet breakfast was served al fresco. Evening meals showcasing local produce and wines are also a highlight or you could choose to self-cater and enjoy a typical kiwi barbeque on the deck. Waimanu Lodge is also available for exclusive use by parties of four. This is the ultimate place to take in all that is Northland or relax and simply enjoy the surroundings.

Family pets on site

Breakfast: Continental
Evening meal: $25-65pp
Guest rooms:
Ambience:
Setting/location:

Accommodation available (NZ$)			+		
2 S/C unit	$220-320	$220-320	$40	Q or Q+S	EN

Cooked breakfast – extra charge.

Coastal Chalet Suites

Leonie Mateer
348 Wainui Road, Whangaroa, Bay of Islands
Tel: 09 4051192   Mob: 0210661358
she-designs@xtra.co.nz
www.lodgings.co.nz – keyword: coastalchalet

Property features
Handcrafted designer kitchens
Open plan tiled bathrooms
Private decks with harbour views
Barbeques, Sky TV, DVD, movies
Hot tub in all suites
Local features
Walk to St Pauls Rock
Tauranga Bay - 8 mins drive
Whangaroa Harbour - 5 mins drive
On scenic loop to Matauri Bay
25 mins Kauri Cliffs golf course

Kaeo - 10 mins drive
Kerikeri - 28 mins drive

Take SH 10 north to Kaeo, 3kms nort
of Kaeo at bridge, continue straight
towards Whangaroa for 4kms. Turn
right on Wainui Road. Coastal chalet
Guest House is 3.48 Kms on right.

Situated only a few Kilometers from the world renowned harbour and gamefishing centre of Whangaroa, it was only a few minutes before I was entering the gates and driving through the beautiful gardens to the chalets to be greeted by Leonie. Little did I know then, how delighted we would be with our home for the next few days. On entering the largest of the three chalets the overwhelming sense of pure luxury and style overtakes all else. From the gourmet kitchen, with double oven, icemaker and every conceivable appliance, enough to delight any foodie, to the library of movies, the pure luxury of top quality linens and the fireplace, and did I mention the bathroom, pure indulgence. All chalets while completely private have their own entertaining areas. Coastal Chalets is the perfect base to make the most of all that is on offer in this area, numerous golf courses including Kauri Cliff, game fishing, the meeting of the seas at Cape Reinga, numerous beaches or walks or you can just simply relax. What can be wrong with a wine in the spa, the sun going down on the deck discussing the one that got away or the one that rolled around the pin. Leonie is the perfect host and she describes Coastal Chalets as "affordable luxury" – what an understatement.

Accommodation available (NZ$)	👤	👥	+👤	🛏	🛁	
1 Suite	$290	$290	$55	K,Q,Q,SB	EN, PR	Breakfast: Provisions provided
1 Suite	$200	$200		Q,D,SB	EN, PR	
1 Suite	$200	$200		K	EN	Guest rooms:

Cot, fishing rods, kayaks available, wireless internet. Daily cleaning service available $25 per day

Ambience:
Setting/location:

LOW   HIGH

Property features
Stunning sea views
3 safe sandy swimming beaches
Beach towels supplied
Complimentary port & chocolates
All balcony rooms
CD/Sky TV/tea/coffee
Local features
Fishing/diving (Rainbow Warrior)
Kayaking/swimming/walking
Golf course/sailing

Huntaway Lodge
Diane & David Lennan
1692 Wainui Road, Te Ngaere Bay, Northland
Tel: 09 4051611
Fax: 09 4051612
info@huntawaylodge.com
www.lodgings.co.nz – keyword: huntaway

Kerikeri - 25 mins drive
Kaeo - 20 mins drive

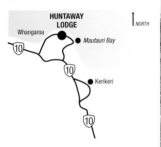

On SH 10 turn right to Matauri Bay, travel 14 km's then turn left in to Wainui Road. Drive through Te Ngaere Bay 600 metres past last house on left turn left up hill.

The road rises from sea level to the contemporary lodge perched high on the hill with 180-degree panoramic views of golden sandy beaches, rocky promontories and the fabulous Cavalli Islands. Nestled up here amongst the beautifully landscaped gardens and well away from any disturbance, it was easy to think that I was on cloud nine. The five guest rooms of this purpose built lodge are romantically named after the beaches and islands viewed from the individual bedroom windows and decks - Te Ngaere, Pia Pia, Wainui, Motueka and Cavalli. All rooms are designed and furnished in a contemporary style with pacific artworks which complement the views and restful atmosphere. Walk in showers are a feature of each ensuite bathroom. Adjoining the guest suites is a spacious open plan lounge and dining area, leading to extensive open decking. This is where guests enjoy al fresco dining and sample the delicious menus using the freshest of ingredients prepared by the resident chef. Diane has worked extensively in the hospitality industry and creates an atmosphere which is relaxing and prefect for unwinding. It was easy just to sit and enjoy the view but if you suddenly feel like a touch of adventure then some of the options are fishing charters, dive the wreck of the Rainbow Warrior with qualified PADI dive operators, or take a Heli-Tour of the Far North. It's all here.

Accommodation available (NZ$)	👤	👤👤	+👤	🛏	🛁
1 Room	$595	$595		Q	EN
2 Rooms	$495	$495		Q+K	EN
2 Rooms	$695	$695		K	EN

Breakfast: Special cooked
Evening meal: $90pp
Guest rooms:
Ambience:
Setting/location:

LOW   HIGH

Magic Cottage

Ian and Anna Sizer
660 Takou Bay Road, SH 10, Kerikeri
Tel: 09 4078065   Mob: 0275457633
takouriver@xtra.co.nz
www.lodgings.co.nz – keyword: magic

Property features
Beautiful river frontage
Clawfoot bath on deck over river
Completely private and secluded
Extensive gardens/boathouse/jetty
Swimming/kayaking/fishing in river
Local features
Beaches and coastal scenery
Fishing/sailing/diving/surfing
Kerikeri, Russell & Waitangi
Golf Courses including Kauri Cliffs
Access to Takou Bay beach

Kerikeri - 20 mins drive
Paihia - 40 mins drive

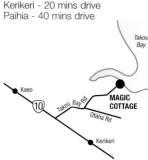

Travelling north from Kerikeri on
SH10, turn right onto Takou Bay Rd
8km beyond Waipapa. Turn left after
1km. Continue on unsealed road.
Property is at very end.

Magic Cottage is a beautiful, romantic and secluded riverside retreat. We enjoyed total privacy in this wonderful studio cottage perched on the banks of the Takou River. Surrounded by 5 acres of beautiful subtropical gardens, the cottage spills onto a deck featuring an antique claw foot bath overlooking the river, the perfect place to relax, gaze at the stars or watch the abundant birdlife as the river slips by. Peace, seclusion and tranquillity surround Magic Cottage. With its secluded swimming, sub-tropical gardens, summer house, private jetty, boat house, fishing, kayaks and the beautiful beach at Takou Bay a short paddle downstream, why would we venture any further? Ian and Anna have a passion for the environment and have planted over 4,000 native trees, converted the 150 acre property to certified organic status and installed solar lighting in Magic Cottage, just a few of the many activities they've undertaken to make the property and your stay as sustainable as possible. Centrally located to explore the wider Bay of Islands and Far North's attractions, Magic Cottage is the perfect retreat hidden away from the hustle and bustle of major tourist towns.

Accommodation available (NZ$)	🧍	🧍🧍	+🧍	🛏	🛁
1 S/C cottage		$190-220		SK/T	EN	Breakfast: Not available

Guest rooms:
Ambience:
Setting/location:

LOW   HIGH

Magic Cottage sleeps two people only.

Property features
River frontage and gardens
150 acre organic property
Claw foot bath in summer house
Jetty & boathouse
Swimming/kayaking/fishing in river
Access to Takou Bay beach
Local features
Beaches/coastal scenery
Fishing/sailing/diving/surfing/golf
Kerikeri/Waitangi/Russell

Takou River Lodge Cottages
Ian and Anna Sizer
660 Takou Bay Road, SH 10, Kerikeri
Tel: 09 4078065   Mob: 0275457633
takouriver@xtra.co.nz
www.lodgings.co.nz – keyword: takouriverlodge

Kerikeri - 20 mins drive
Paihia - 40 mins drive

Travelling north from Kerikeri on
SH10, turn right onto Takou Bay Rd
8km beyond Waipapa. Turn left after
1km. Continue on unsealed road.
Property is at very end.

If you have ever wanted the perfect escape, Takou River Cottages provide the answer.The two purpose designed cottages are set amid 5 acres of sub-tropical gardens bounded by the Takou River, and surrounded by 150 acres of organic farmland. A stunning alfresco claw foot bath on the deck of the private summer house overlooks the gardens and river and adds to the sense of peace, calm and relaxation. I admire the hosts Ian and Anna's passion for travel and the environment evident from the beautiful recycled timber floors, artefacts from their work and travel, and the thousands of native trees which they have planted while converting their 150 acre property to organic status. Each cottage comprises two ensuite double bedrooms and a spacious hallway which leads upstairs to a light, airy open plan kitchen, living and dining area with private sundeck and river and garden views. These two cottages were so quiet and peaceful I never wanted to leave. I had plenty of time to enjoy long walks through the lush sub-tropical gardens, paddle along the river and dream or read beside the ponds. Kayaks and canoes are available for guests' use, ideal for heading down the river to the beautiful and deserted beach close by at Takou Bay.

Accommodation available (NZ$)	👤	👤👤	+👤	🛏	🛁
2 S/C cottages		$220	$40-50	K/T+Q	EN

Breakfast: Not available

Guest rooms:
Ambience:
Setting/location:

Low season and long stay rates available.

Cavalli View Cottage

Sharon Burges Rick Harris
27 Te Ra Road, Takou Bay, Kerikeri
Tel: 09 4079019   Mob: 0211185047
Fax: 09 4079018
cavallicottage@hotmail.com
www.lodgings.co.nz – keyword: cavalliview

Property features
Ocean/island views
Peaceful private setting
Self contained
Decks and barbecue
Clawfoot bath on deck-hot/cold water
Local features
Close to Kauri Cliffs golf course
Whangaroa Harbour/game fishing
Kerikeri
Wineries/art and craft centre
Kauri Forrest

Kerikeri - 20 mins drive
Whangarei - 80 mins drive

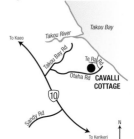

Turn right off SH 10 north of Kerikeri
onto Takou Bay Rd. Take right fork to
Otaha Road. After 4kms turn left into
Te Ra Rd. Go half km and fork left
onto Te Ra Extension. 3rd drive on
left. Cottage is at end of drive.

As I turned off the highway and headed towards the coast of Takou bay I realised I was heading for a place with awesome views over a delightful beach. Cavalli View Cottage is set in a peaceful, spacious garden surrounded by fruit orchards and native plantings and is completely separate from the hosts' home. There is an array of birdlife, the Tui being a frequent visitor to the surrounding Bottlebrushes. The warm interior has a tranquil atmosphere and features an abundance of natural oiled timber. Bi-fold windows open from the lounge/dining area onto a sweeping expanse of lawn which looks towards the ocean and beyond to the majestic Cavalli Islands silhouetted against the horizon. A spacious queen-size bedroom opens onto an expansive deck where there is a traditional clawfoot bath complete with hot and cold taps for relaxing under the stars with a nightcap before retiring. A barbecue is provided along with outdoor furniture for private alfresco dining. You can completely self-cater in the neat fully equipped kitchen or choose to eat out at one of the many restaurants in Kerikerei. There are several golf courses in the area the closest being the world class Kauri Cliffs and there are no shortages of idyllic beaches in the vicinity.

Accommodation available (NZ$)	👤	👤👤	+👤	🛏	🛁	Family pets on site Guest pets by arrangement
1 S/C cottage		$150-170		Q	PR	Breakfast: Not available

Portable beds available in cottage.

Guest rooms:
Ambience:
Setting/location:

LOW   HIGH

Property features
Spectacular sea views
Secluded beach
Bush walks
Kiwi habitat
Stream and waterfall
Local features
Historic sites/buildings
Boating/fishing/diving/kauri forest
Several golf courses nearby
Boutique chocolate factory
Art & craft galleries

Fernbrook
Robert and Margaret Cooper
Kurapari Road, RD 1, Rangitane, Kerikeri
Tel: 09 4078570
Fax: 09 4078572
tfc@igrin.co.nz
www.lodgings.co.nz – keyword: fernbrook

Kerikeri - 12 mins drive
Whangarei - 1 hr 15 mins drive

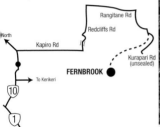

Take SH 10 past the Kerkeri turnoff, through Waipapa township for 1km and right into Kapiro Rd. After 4.5km turn left on Redcliffs Rd and follow signs to Rangitane. Turn right into Kurapari Rd for 300 mtrs. Second driveway on right.

The drive through the country lanes North East of Kerikeri inlet towards Fernbrook gives only a hint of the lushness of the 27ha sanctuary that Robert and Margaret have created over a number of years. Driving up the tree lined driveway does not prepare one for the breathtaking water views and extensive gardens that stretch out to the inlet. Fernbrook offers accommodation to suit every requirement. The luxurious beach front two bedroom cottage steeped in history was a perfect place to unwind for a few days. The tide came and went to reveal an ever changing vista of birdlife and moods. Other choices included a one bedroom self contained apartment or two other beautifully appointed guest rooms from where you can simply relax, enjoy the surroundings, antique furnishings and a well appointed library. Robert and Margaret have spent countless hours on regenerating the native habit, ensuring the sustainability of the native bird life including the North Island brown kiwi, which can be heard calling after dark. Numerous golf courses and beaches are an easy drive away, as is the historic town of Kerikeri. However you may like us choose to just wander the numerous tracks on the property, pick the spoils of Robert and Margaret's labour from the orchards and simply enjoy their company.

Accommodation available (NZ$)	👤	👤👤	+👤	🛏	🛁
1 S/C unit	$250	$300		Q	EN
1 S/C cottage	$300	$450-500		K+Q	EN
1 Suite	$220	$240		Q	EN
1 Room	$220	$220		Q	PR
S/C cottage has two bedrooms.					

Breakfast: Cooked
Evening Meal: $60pp
Guest rooms:
Ambience:
Setting/location:

LOW   HIGH

21

William and Mary's

Mary and Bill Fenton
24 Access Heights, Kerikeri
Tel: 09 4071117   Mob: 021722938
Fax: 09 4075117
maryfenton@hotmail.com
www.lodgings.co.nz – keyword: williammary

Property features
Full kitchen/laundry/heat pumps
Spa bath
Barbeque/kayaks
Golf course and river views
Three TV's
Local features
Kayaking in adjacent river
Golf course adjacent, 2 nearby
Shopping - 3 mins drive
Historic Stone Store - 7mins drive

Kerikeri - 3 mins drive
Paihia - 25 mins drive

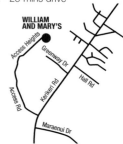

From Whangarei take SH1 north through Kawakawa. At Pakaraka turn right onto SH10 and travel 18kms. Turn right onto Kerikeri Road. Access Road 2km on your left. Access Heights veers right at the end. Go to end of this Rd

William and Mary's is situated in the heart of Kerikeri however you could be forgiven for thinking that you are miles from anywhere. It is just so peaceful. This new, very spacious two bedroom cottage is on the banks of a stream which overlooks the water features of the Kerikeri Golf Course. Mary and Bill have thought of everything, huge designer kitchen, two luxurious bathrooms and full length decking, and even a time out room for reading and catching up on business if you must. Thoughtful extras are everywhere, home made preserves, flowers, chocolates and luxury toiletries. If the splendid view out over the golf course doesn't lure you out to play then there are kayaks at the bottom of the garden to explore the two kilometres of the meandering stream which is full of bird life. Kerikeri is the fruit bowl and art centre of the North and the township is just three minutes drive with a multitude of cafés and specialty stores. Mary and Bill are wonderful, warm hosts; they live up the driveway and are on hand to assist with any bookings, trip planning or advice on local attractions. William and Mary's, an ecologically friendly haven is the perfect base for up to two couples to stay a few days and make it your home away from home in Northland.

Accommodation available (NZ$)	👤	👤👤	+👤	🛏	🛁	Guest pets by arrangement
1 S/C house	$300-500			SK or 2S EN		Breakfast: Continental
				SK or 2S EN		

House has two bedrooms/study. Seasonal rates apply.

Guest rooms:
Ambience:
Setting/location:

LOW   HIGH

Property features
Well appointed guest rooms
Separate guest lounge
TV/Video/DVD/guest computer
Exquisite french décor
Local features
Historic stone store
River basin - 5 mins walk
Restaruant/cafes - 5 mins walk
Game fishing/boating/swimming
Kauri Cliff golf course

Bed of Roses
Louisa and Cliff Hobson-Corry
165 Kerikeri Road, Kerikeri
Tel: 09 4074666   Mob: 0274949062
bedofroses@xtra.co.nz
www.lodgings.co.nz – keyword: bedofroses

Ⓟ ✉

Card   MasterCard   **VISA**   eftpos

Kerikeri - 5 mins walk
Paihia - 20 mins drive

From Whangarei take SH1 north
to Pakaraka. Turn right onto SH10
and travel 18kms. Turn right onto
Kerikeri Road. Bed of Roses is at
the end of the village on the right
past the Northland Polytechnic.

In the heart of Kerikeri there is a true gem with every comfort, everything you could wish for. Bed of Roses as the name suggests is for the very discerning traveller. Louisa and Cliff have been in the hospitality industry for over 20 years and their experience shows. No expense has been spared to ensure that their guests are pampered, from the beautiful white linen, luxurious towels and toiletries, exquisite china to the French county antique furniture. I particularly loved the Monet Suite and immediately thought I was back in Provence. Kerikeri is an oasis of exotic tropical plantings where it appears everything will flourish. The original stone store, just a short walk from Bed of Roses was the beginning of what is now a vibrant town full of cafés, galleries and Kerikeri has become a fruit bowl of superb produce. Louisa draws on this to create her renowned breakfasts. Passionate about food and presentation, the menu changes daily and is all homemade. I sat on the sun drenched terrace over looking the yachts moored in the inlet. The smell of freshly baked bread wafted from the kitchen and I could not help but feel that this was a little bit of France in Kerikeri.

Breakfast: Cooked

Guest rooms:
Ambience:
Setting/location:

LOW   HIGH

Accommodation available (NZ$)	👤	👤👤	+👤	🛏	🛁
1 Cottage	$250	$325	$50	K+D	EN
1 Room	$210	$295	$50	Q+S	EN
1 Room	$200	$275		Q	EN

23

Paheke

Juen and Frank Duxfield
103 State Highway 1, Ohaeawai, Bay of Islands
Tel: 09 4059623   Mob: 0274485780
Fax: 09 4059628
paheke@xtra.co.nz
www.lodgings.co.nz – keyword: paheke

Property features
1862 - historic character house
Spacious park like gardens
Barbeque area for guests
Petanque court
Cedar of Lebanon - 140 yrs old
Local features
World-class golf courses - 10 mins
Walking tracks - 20 mins
Geological rock features - 30 mins
Begonia gardens - 10 mins
Historic sites - 10 mins drive

Kaikohe - 10 mins drive
Kerikeri - 15 mins drive

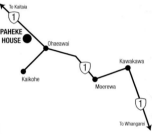

On SH 1 three hours drive north
of Auckland Airport pass through
the small settlement of Ohaeawai.
Paheke is one kilometre further on
the left.

Surrounded by a two-and-a-half acre area of enchanting gardens shaded by enormous old trees, The Paheke Homestead brings a slower, more peaceful era, to mind. The house was built in 1862 and, together with the dominating Lebanon cedar tree in the front garden, is New Zealand historic Places trust listed. Frank and Juen welcomed me enthusiastically and after tea I was invited to share the living spaces and verandahs of their comfortable house and wander the charming garden. The well-proportioned rooms of the old house are filled with interesting antique furniture which the couple has collected over many years, but the main accommodation is in the new wing which was seamlessly added in to the house in the old style but with modern convenience and luxuries. The bedrooms are large and airy with views out onto the tranquil gardens. I joined them for a glass of wine before dinner and the next day enjoyed a picnic in the garden. Like many others I left with warm memories.

Accommodation available (NZ$)	🧍	🧍🧍	+🧍	🛏	🛁	Family dog on site Guest pets by arrangement
1 Room	$185	$185	$35	K	EN	Breakfast: Cooked
1 Room	$150	$150	$35	Q	EN	Evening meal: $60pp
1 Room	$150	$150		D	EN	Guest rooms:
1 Room	$150	$150	$35	Q+S	PR	Ambience:
						Setting/location:

LOW   HIGH

Property features
Extensive sea views
Private decks with all day sun
Nautical theme
Ensuite to each bedroom
Off site host-guests privacy
Local features
Central Bay of Islands location
Boat trips/sailing/fishing
Historic attractions
Golf course/sightseeing

Crows Nest Villas

Marj Browning
20 Sir George Back Street, Opua, Bay of Islands
Tel: 09 4027783   Mob: 0272105242
Fax: 09 4027783
marj@vivid.net.nz
www.lodgings.co.nz – keyword: crowsnest

Paihia - 5 mins drive
Whangarei - 45 mins drive

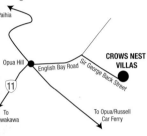

On SH11 from Kawakawa travel 15 mins to Opua hill. Cross into English Bay Rd, take the first right into Sir George Back St. Number 20 at end of cul-de-sac.

Hidden in the hills overlooking Opua harbour, the Crows Nest Villas are named to reflect a nautical theme. The Bridge Deck and Sails both have breathtaking views and a casual, contemporary feel. The self-contained villas had everything I needed for a weekend escape and were private enough for a romantic getaway or perfect for two families. Each bedroom within the villas has its own ensuite. As there was a barbecue available at Bridge Deck I decided to cook for myself while I enjoyed the afternoon sun. The shops in Paihia were an easy five-minute drive away and I found everything there that I needed for a good New Zeland barbecue. If you are looking for a break from cooking however, Marj, who is the host, is only too happy to organise restaurant dining for the evening. After dinner I lazed on the sumptuous leather sofas, reading books and watching the boats come and go through Opua port. The following day I visited historic Russell, only a short ferry ride away and enjoyed the sights and restaurants.

Accommodation available (NZ$)	👤	👤👤	+👤	🛏	🛁
1 S/C house			$305-575	2Q	2EN
1 S/C house			$225-495	Q+2S	2EN

Breakfast: Provisions provided

Guest rooms:
Ambience:
Setting/location:

Provisions supplied first morning only. Offseason rates available.

25

Flagstaff Lodge & Day Spa

Darryl Smith and Beth Strickland
17 Wellington Street, Russell, Bay of Islands
Tel: 09 4037117   Mob: 0275521246
Fax: 09 4037817   Free: 0800403711
info@flagstafflodge.co.nz
www.lodgings.co.nz – keyword: flagstaff

Property features
Day spa/massage
Outdoor baths/beauty treatments
Guest lounge
Exquisite furnishings
Local features
Russell museum - 5 mins walk
Russell wharf - 5 mins walk
Russell galleries - 5 mins walk
Restaruants / cafes - 5 mins walk

Russell - 2 mins walk
Auckland - 3 hrs 30 mins drive

From Opua car ferry, follow Aucks rd for appox 8km onto Russell rd, left at Hope avenue, left at Brind rd, right on Guild st, left onto Chapel st, right into Beresford st, then left into Wellington

Russell, steeped in history is a picturesque town in the world renowned Bay of Islands. Flagstaff Lodge & Day Spa, a 1912 villa situated in the heart of Russell is a part of this history offering luxury accommodation for a maximum of 8 people. The four spacious rooms each have a distinctive New Zealand theme and are furnished with the most exquisite fabric's and paint finishes. There is the Pacific, Pohutukawa and the Strand however I stepped into my room; the Sunset room with its gold and coral décor and the "wow factor" takes over. Drop dead gorgeous to say the least. It wasn't long before I joined our hosts Darryl and Beth in the guest lounge for evening drinks before taking the 100 metre stroll to the waterfront to enjoy the cafés and galleries. Russell is the perfect place to stop and explore. There are fishing charters, swimming with the dolphins, golf, historic trails and wonderful art galleries to name but a few activities. You could also curl up and read or take in a DVD in front of the fire however I had booked a massage at the in-house spa for the late afternoon. The range of treatments by professional therapists is vast using the very best of products. Relax under the stars with champagne in the matching claw foot baths. Flagstaff Lodge has it all and if it is pampering that you want then you have come to the right place.

Accommodation available (NZ$)	🧍	🧍🧍	+🧍	🛏	🛁			
2 Rooms	$585	$650		SK	EN	Breakfast: Cooked		
2 Rooms	$495	$550		SK	EN			
1 S/C house		$2,600		4xSK	EN,PR	Guest rooms:		
						Ambience:		
						Setting/location:		

LOW   HIG

Property features
Flora - Fauna
Native bush view
Privacy assured
Numerous walking tracks
Kayaks for guest use
Local features
Beaches nearby
Estuaries
Conservation values

Ara Roa
Paul and Susanne Olsen
54 Harambee Road, Taiharuru, Whangarei
Tel: 09 4365028   Mob: 0273200770
Fax: 09 4365028
info@araroa.co.nz
www.lodgings.co.nz – keyword: araroa

Whangarei - 30 mins drive
Auckland - 2 hours drive

From Whangarei, take the road to
Onerahi. Turn left to Whangarei Heads
to Parua Bay. Follow the road to Pataua
for 4km, take the Taiharuru Rd turnoff
on your right. Harambee Road is the
2nd on your right approx 4km - No 54

The picturesque drive along the stretches of the Whangarei Harbour to Ara Roa is only a slight indication of what is to come. Up and over the hill and into Harambee Road then up the kilometre long driveway past our hosts Paul and Susanne Olsen's home - nearly there now. The sky is the limit. Stepping out of the car and turning around, the view explodes before you over the valleys towards the estuary and finally out to the Pacific Ocean. This luxury two bedroom self contained guest house has absolutely everything for the discerning guest. Fully equipped kitchen, luxurious bath overlooking the native bush, spacious bedrooms and colourful artworks adorning the walls. There is even broadband if I really wanted to waste time as there are so many other options. Take the kayaks and explore the estuary, or wander along the rolling ocean beach. Some days I was the only one on it, certainly not every man and his dog, and speaking of dogs they must stay home as being surrounded by bush there is a large range of native birds that can be observed at quite close range including Kiwi calling, sometimes very near the house. This is an area noted for its high ecological values. Paul and Susanne have a surcharge for a one night stay and you will never want to pay it as this is the ideal place to chill out for weeks.

Accommodation available (NZ$)					
Breakfast: Not available	1 S/C cottage	$190-310	$45	K+Q+2S	PR

Guest rooms:
Ambience:
Setting/location:

LOW   HIGH

Breakaway Retreat

Sheelagh and Mark Prosser
1856 Whangarei Heads Road,
McLeod Bay, Whangarei
Tel: 09 4340711   Mob: 0273318009
breakaway@breakawayretreat.co.nz
www.lodgings.co.nz – keyword: breakawayretreat

Property features
Beachfront location
Stunning sea views
2 kayaks with life jackets
Safe swimming area
Local features
Swimming and surf beaches
Places to launch/anchor boat
Fishing, boating/sailing
Windsurfing/waterskiing/diving
Bushwalks/golf/tennis

Whangarei - 25 mins drive
Auckland - 150 mins drive

From Whangarei follow signs to Onerah
turn left onto Whangarei Heads Rd.
Continue past Parua Bay Shopping
Centre. Continue on the Whangarei
Heads Rd until you reach the McLeod
Bay 50km sign. We are second entranc
on the right after the sign. No 1856

The very aptly named Breakaway Retreat Guest House located just 30kms East of Whangarei is situated only 20 meters from the beach. Drive down the tree lined driveway and you are in another world. Sheelagh and Mark who live next door, are on hand to greet us. We stepped inside and could not resist going straight out onto the expansive deck to smell the sea and take in the view. The children were out the door and down the track to the beach quick smart. This tastefully furnished, two bedroom, self contained guest house with spacious open plan living area is fully equipped with every possible amenity to make our stay perfect including spa bath, kayaks and a barbeque. There was so much to do in this beautiful part of the country and we had no trouble filling in our days swimming, fishing from the rocks, snorkelling, walking Mt Manaia and over to nearby Smugglers Bay. Sheelagh and Mark were wonderful hosts and only to happy to assist with advice. We found at the end of our day it was just wonderful to sit back on the deck with a wine and listen to the water lapping almost at our feet and take in the tranquility of this wonderful haven. This was a perfect place to put our feet down and spend a few days after travelling. We also declared we would come back for a romantic few days.

Accommodation available (NZ$)						Family cat on site
S/C house		$250-290	$45	K+2S	PR	Breakfast: Continental

Guest rooms:
Ambience:
Setting/location:

Continental breakfast supplied for your first morning.

Property features
Private bay for swimming/boating
Private beach with 20 acres
Open fire for winter atmosphere
WiFi internet and SKY TV
Restored historic cottage
Mooring up to 10 metres available

Local features
Fishing off Parua Bay Jetty
Restaurants in close proximity
Beach walks/golf course
Diving/fishing/hiking reserves

Whangarei - 20 mins drive
Auckland - 2 hrs 30 mins drive

Parua Bay Cottage
Greg and Marian Innes
Parua Cemetery Rd, Parua Bay, Whangarei Heads
Tel: 09 4365626   Mob: 0274953382
Free: 0800116626
paruabaycottage@innes-strategy.com
www.lodgings.co.nz – keyword: paruabay

From Whangarei, follow signs to Whangarei Heads. Pass Parua Bay Tavern and turn second right into Parua Cemetery Rd. Follow to the beach - the cottage is on your right.

Parua Bay Cottage is located adjacent to a beach shared only with the Innes family. The beach is sandy and is suitable for swimming, fishing, lazing on, and all this not fifty steps from the cottage. The view from the front door is of the beach framed by pohutukawa, while the view from the back door is of the large native tree block behind. The cottage has recently been renovated and has plenty of space for a long summer holiday. There are two bedrooms, a lounge with open fire, dining room and kitchen, bathroom and full laundry. All I needed to bring was plenty of food and wine. Despite being over 120 years old, the cottage had every amenity I needed - the new kitchen comes complete with gas hobs and oven. Marian has, however, gone to a lot of trouble to have everything in keeping with the age of the cottage. There was plenty for this city dweller to do here: bushwalking, birdwatching, feeding the chickens/ducks, beach activities, or relaxing on the verandah reading a good book. Children and/or dogs are most welcome here. This is quite unlike so many seaside experiences - no crowds, no noise - if you can't relax here you need help.

Family pets on site
Guest pets by arrangement

Breakfast: Not included

Guest rooms:
Ambience:
Setting/location:

LOW   HIGH

Accommodation available (NZ$)	👤	👥	+👤	🛏	🛁
1 S/C cottage	$195	$195	$30	2D+3S	PR
(5 nights)	$150	$150	$30		
1 S/C off season	$160	$160	$30		

Safe and private beach/bay with mooring.

Lake House

Chris and Susan Alves
212 Pukeatua Road, Maungatapere, Whangarei
Tel: 09 4348084   Mob: 0210647673
Fax: 09 4348084
unwind@lakehouse.net.nz
www.lodgings.co.nz – keyword: lakehouse

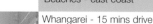

Property features
Spectacular lakeside setting
Swimming pool/sun drenched deck
English and European Antiques
Private and tranquil
Suitable for disabled
Local features
Bush walks/ horse riding/golf
Boat trips/deep sea fishing/diving
Museum - 10 mins drive
Kauri Forest - west coast
Beaches - east coast
Whangarei - 15 mins drive
Waipoua Forest - 1 hour drive

From Whangarei follow SH14 towards
Maungatapere. 1km past the village turn
left into Pukeatua Road. Proceed 1.6km
and as rising from dip, the Lake House
is the second driveway on the right.

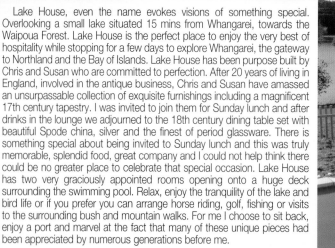

Lake House, even the name evokes visions of something special. Overlooking a small lake situated 15 mins from Whangarei, towards the Waipoua Forest. Lake House is the perfect place to enjoy the very best of hospitality while stopping for a few days to explore Whangarei, the gateway to Northland and the Bay of Islands. Lake House has been purpose built by Chris and Susan who are committed to perfection. After 20 years of living in England, involved in the antique business, Chris and Susan have amassed an unsurpassable collection of exquisite furnishings including a magnificent 17th century tapestry. I was invited to join them for Sunday lunch and after drinks in the lounge we adjourned to the 18th century dining table set with beautiful Spode china, silver and the finest of period glassware. There is something special about being invited to Sunday lunch and this was truly memorable, splendid food, great company and I could not help think there could be no greater place to celebrate that special occasion. Lake House has two very graciously appointed rooms opening onto a huge deck surrounding the swimming pool. Relax, enjoy the tranquility of the lake and bird life or if you prefer you can arrange horse riding, golf, fishing or visits to the surrounding bush and mountain walks. For me I choose to sit back, enjoy a port and marvel at the fact that many of these unique pieces had been appreciated by numerous generations before me.

Accommodation available (NZ$)	🧍	🧍🧍	+🧍	🛏	🛁	Family cat on site
1 Room	$235	$255	SK	EN		
1 Room	$235	$255	SK/2KS	EN		

Breakfast: Special Cooked
Evening meal: $50
Guest rooms:
Ambience:
Setting/location:

LOW   HIGH

Ironing board, laundry facilities and wireless internet available.

Property features
25 year old historic Kauri lodge
Guest lounge/bar/library/cosy fire
Separate, private, luxury suites
Overlooking the forest
Chef/kitchen garden/finest cuisine
Bush walks/extensive gardens
Local features
Waipoua & Trounson Kauri Forests
Kai Iwi Lakes - swimming, kayaking
Private guides, Kiwi in the wild
Golden sand beaches.

Dargaville - 40 mins drive
Hokianga Harbour - 40 mins drive

Take Highway 1 north to the
Brynderwyns. Follow the "Twin Coast
Discovery" signs to Dargaville. Take
State Highway 12 north toward the
Waipoua Forest. The lodge is 47kms
from Dargaville on the main highway
on the right hand side.

Waipoua Lodge

Nicole and Chris Donahoe
State Highway 12, Waipoua Forest, Northland
Tel: 09 4390422
Fax: 09 5238081
lodgings@waipoualodge.co.nz
www.lodgings.co.nz – keyword: waipoualodge

ⓟ 🚶 ✉ 📺   💳 💳 VISA eftpos 💳 💳 ♨

An absolute calm surrounds this majestic kauri villa, overlooking the Waipoua Forest that stretches out to the horizon. Waipoua Lodge is perfectly positioned for access to lakes and the golden sand beaches nearby, as well as the famous tree 'Tane Mahuta'. The welcome and charm of Nicole and Chris immediately put me at ease. My niece was travelling with me and, with children of their own, she was warmly welcomed. Nicole guided me to our spacious suite with balcony overlooking the forest and gardens. Housed within the original farm buildings, each has been distinctly styled with quality furnishings and attention to detail. My niece was delighted with the large bath and loft in our suite. It was so relaxing, fresh baking and flowers in my room, there were CD's to listen to, and later, I relaxed with a DVD in the quiet of my room. A memorable dinner served by candle light, focused on local produce and fresh organic vegetables from the garden - a daily menu appeared each afternoon featuring three entrees, a main course of the finest meats and seafood, vegetables and locally grown kumara prepared by their helpful chef. After a difficult choice between three desserts, I finished with an espresso and a fine brandy by the lodge fire - totally satiated. This understated, gracious and relaxed lodge offers luxury and peace to anyone travelling the unspoiled Kauri Coast.

Family outside dog on site

Breakfast: Full Breakfast
Evening Meal: $90pp
Guest rooms:
Ambience:
Setting/location:

LOW   HIGH

Accommodation available (NZ$)	🧍	🧍🧍	+🧍	🛏	🛁
2 S/C suites	$470-550	$490-570		K or 2S	EN
1 S/C suite		$540-590	$80	2K or 4S	EN
1 S/C suite		$540-590	$80	K or 2S+2S	EN

Stereo/DVD's/CD's, kitchenette in each cottage. Children welcome, under 6 are free.

31

Great Barrier Island

Warkworth

Matakana

Kumeu

Bethells
Beach

Auckland

Waimana Point

Gloria and Geoff Collier
35 Martins Bay Road, RD2, Warkworth
Tel: 09 4255102   Mob: 0274971535
Fax: 09 4255203
info@waimanapoint.co.nz
www.lodgings.co.nz – keyword: waimana

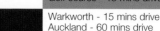

Property features
Indoor heated lap pool/small gym
Sauna/outdoor baths on private deck
Private beach access
Swimming/kayaking/petanque
Separate guest lounge/Sky tv/DVD/stereo
Local features
Scandrett Regional Park
Vineyards/wineries
Cafes/restaurants
Farmers markets - 15 mins drive
Golf course - 15 mins drive

Warkworth - 15 mins drive
Auckland - 60 mins drive

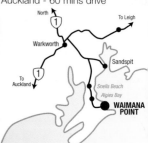

From Warkworth take the road to
Sandspit-Snells Algies. Drive throug
Snells and Algies. The driveway is
one km on left past Algies heading
towards Martins Bay. Drive down
long drive to end of point.

Placed anywhere, Waimana Point lodge would receive accolades for quality of construction, for sheer style, facilities and comfort. Placed on Waimana Point, above Kawau Bay, it is a jewel. Exhilarating water views, the seascape dotted with small islets framed by a magnificent backdrop of Kawau Bay. The Lodge offers privacy, seclusion and exclusivity with its unique location set on a wonderful 17 acre coastal point. This is a place of re-discovery, of quiet contemplation and of space to oneself. Feeling the need to exercise or explore, one might stroll to the beach – there are complimentary kayaks – or continue the coastal walk to a regional park. Beach swimming or rock fishing for the adventurous, or maybe keeping in trim at the lodge's heated lap pool. Such a splendid facility, yet with such a gentle footprint. For this Lodge is largely eco self sufficient with its own water and sewage systems, its own garden and farm produce. "We mostly catch our own fish, too", confides Geoff. Waimana really is a special place, deserving of special people, seeking somewhere extraordinary to mark a special occasion.

Accommodation available (NZ$)					
3 S/C Suites	$450-545	SK or 2S	EN		
1 S/C Suite	$480-575	2SK or 4S	EN		

Breakfast: Enquire
Evening meal: $60pp
Guest rooms:
Ambience:
Setting/location:

Equipped for small conferences and functions.
Evening meals Mon-Fri by arrangement.

LOW   HIG

34

Property features
Secluded, tranquil position
Views of estuary and vineyard
Landscaped grounds
Separate guest lounge

Local features
Pottery and craft - 10 min drive
Vineyards/wineries/restaurants
Seashore/café - 10 min walk
Harbour Cruises - 10 min walk
Golf course/beaches/movie theatres
Marine reserve diving/sailing

The Saltings Estate
Terry and Maureen Baines
1210 Sandspit Road, Sandspit, Warkworth
Tel: 09 4259670   Mob: 021625948
Fax: 09 4259674
relax@saltings.co.nz
www.lodgings.co.nz – keyword: saltings

Warkworth - 7 mins drive
Auckland - 55 mins drive

From Auckland take SH 1 north.
From Warkworth at the second
turn off take right hand road to
Sandspit. Travel 5 mins. Take signs
to Sandspit. The Saltings is on your
right.

I found the Saltings Estate up a meandering tree-lined driveway, where there is a choice of gourmet bed & breakfast at The Saltings or self catering luxury accommodation at The Vintner's Haven. The locality, the light uncluttered interiors and creative paint effects have resulted in unique accommodation of excellent quality. The Saltings and The Vintner's Haven have a Mediterranean ambience and a feeling of romance which is emphasised by the fresh white linens, tiles and soft lighting. Generously proportioned rooms open to their own private courtyard or deck and several have stunning views of the vineyard and estuary. Everything here is presented with consummate good taste and I can particularly recommend Maureen's delicious organic based breakfasts using local produce. Terry's vineyard is cultivated using natural methods and biodynamic principles to produce Syrah and Bordeaux blend wines. There is plenty to do in this area: including wine trails, Saturday morning markets, ferry trips to Kawau Island, walks, good restaurants and boutique movie theatres.

Breakfast: Special cooked

Guest rooms:
Ambience:
Setting/location:

LOW   HIGH

Accommodation available (NZ$)	🧍	🧍🧍	+🧍	🛏	🛁
1 Room				K	EN
1 Suite				SK	EN
1 Room				SK	EN
1 S/C Apt			$100	2SK	2EN
1 S/C Apt				Q	EN

1 Room	$235-280	K	EN
1 Suite	$290-395	SK	EN
1 Room	$245-295	SK	EN
1 S/C Apt	$395-650 $100	2SK	2EN
1 S/C Apt	$265-295	Q	EN

Breakfast provisions for S/C Apt.

35

Kourawhero Country Lodge

Gordon and Lorraine Mann, Jenni and Michael Shah
471 Wyllie Road, Warkworth, North Auckland
Tel: 09 4223377   Mob: 0272575100
Fax: 09 4223191   Free: 0800568721
info@kourawhero.co.nz
www.lodgings.co.nz – keyword: kourawhero

Property features
Beautiful country setting
Expansive views of Kawau Island
Heated outdoor swimming pool
Gym/sauna/sanarium
All weather tennis court
Archery/petanque/3 meeting rooms
Jogging circuit/bushwalks
Local features
Matakana wine trail
Matakana farmers market (Sat)

Warkworth - 10 mins drive
Auckland - 1 hour drive

Warkworth is 20 minutes north of Orewa on State Hightway 1. As yo drive into Warkworth turn left into Woodcocks road, continue for 2 km and then turn left into Wyllie road.

Kourawhero situated only one hour north of Auckland and a few minutes from Warkworth and the Matakana wine growing district is a new purpose built lodge, the result of the Mann families' dream. With just eighteen suites in nine chalets dotted over the hillside overlooking the expansive valley and out to the sea the sense of space is overwhelming. The same sense of space prevails on entering the lodge with an enormous fire and adjourning wine cellar. The décor has been chosen to stop you in your tracks and nothing has been spared. It is spectacular and everywhere you look there is an interesting aspect. Our room, looking out to the Hauraki Gulf had received similar treatment – pure indulgence. With on site conference rooms, map room, tennis court, spa and a host of other activities Kourawhero is a destination for weddings, corporate events or just peace and solitude. We ambled down the short distance to the main lodge to join our fellow guests for pre dinner drinks and a magnificent five course dinner. Sustainability is important here including heavy planting of trees many of which produce ingredients for the chef. If all this luxury is not enough there is the 58ft sports fisher for day cruising or for the ultimate in pampered weekends they will transport you from Princess wharf to Warkworth. Spoil yourself!

Accommodation available (NZ$)					
18 Suites	$550	$950		SK	EN

Included in tarrif is a 5 course gourmet dinner, which includes pre dinner drinks.

Breakfast: Special cooked
Evening meal: Included
Guest rooms:
Ambience:
Setting/location:

LOW   HIG

Property features
Tranquil rual & native bush setting
In-house & in-room dining
Generous guest areas
High quality linen, towels & gowns
TV & DVD in rooms
WiFi access

Local features
Wineries/cafes/restaurants
Art/pottery/antiques
Beaches/diving/glass bottom boat
Golf courses

Warkworth - 3 mins drive
Matakana - 8 mins drive

From Auckland, head north on SH1 towards Warkworth, turn right into Matakana Road at the second set of lights. Clayden Road is the second turning on the left.

Gifford Lodge
Edward and Robyn Isherwood
139 Clayden Road, Warkworth 0941
Tel: 09 4259995   Mob: 0274430151
Fax: 09 4250102
info@gifford-lodge.co.nz
www.lodgings.co.nz – keyword: gifford

Time out required from the city or returning from an adventure in Northland, then what better place to stop off than Matakana and Gifford Lodge just 45 minutes north of Auckland. Robyn and Edward are committed hosts and their attention to detail is evident throughout. We were shown to our suite and were delighted with all the little personal touches. The spa bath could wait for later, for now it was time just enjoy our surroundings and take time out and it wasn't long before we were relaxing out on the balcony with a drink admiring the view over the countryside and the stand of native bush. Matakana has emerged as a destiny with an abundance of wineries, arts and crafts, and farmers market. There is no shortage of cafés and Robyn and Edward provided us with expert knowledge of where to go for dinner. A beautifully presented breakfast was served in the dining room and it was a pleasure to sit and talk with our hosts, however the choice was there to have it in our suite. We found Matakana to be the perfect place to end our Northland experience, busy yet peaceful and artistic with style, a reflection of Gifford Lodge really and we left feeling we had made life long friends as they truly are excellent hosts.

Accommodation available (NZ$)	👤	👥	+👤	🛏	🛁
Breakfast: Cooked	1 Suite	$365	$430	$60	SK	EN
Evening meal: $65pp	1 Suite	$275	$340	$60	SK	EN
Guest rooms:	1 Suite	$235	$300	$60	SK or T	PR
Ambience:	2 Suites	$185	$250	$60	K or Q	EN
Setting/location:						

Laundry, transport, internet, computer, telephone available on site.

LOW   HIGH

37

Sugarloaf Lodge

Allan and Vanessa Barber
1068 Leigh Road, Matakana 0948
Tel: 09 4229515   Mob: 0274758992
Fax: 09 4229516
vanessa@sugarloaflodge.co.nz
www.lodgings.co.nz – keyword: sugarloaf

Property features
Magnificent views to Great Barrier
Hill walks/golf bookings
Wine & hors d'oeuvres incl. in tariff
Tennis racquets & court access
Suites separate from house
Local features
Vineyards - 10 mins drive
Cafés and restaurants
Beach walks/golf courses
Tawharanui Regional Park
Farmers Market - 5 mins drive
Warkworth - 10 mins drive
Auckland - 60 mins drive

From Auckland take SH1, drive across
Harbour Bridge to Warkworth - 50
minutes. Turn right at second traffic
lights, following signs to Matakana. Driv
through village, pass the Country Park o
right, 500m is Pukematekeo driveway
and Sugarloaf Lodge sign is on left.

Just out of Matakana, the start of New Zealand's winterless north, there's Sugarloaf hill. A private drive rises from the coastal highway to Allan and Vanessa's built-for-the-view lodge. And what views! On, out over sheltered estuary, Omaha's sweep of ocean beach, to the major islands of Auckland's outer Hauraki Gulf. It is this magnificent vista that demands attention on arrival, to be studied whilst staying and to be looked back on regretfully when leaving. Matakana district's burgeoning art and craft galleries vie for attention with speciality small holdings, vineyards, its sheltered estuaries and wild surf beaches. It's all so close! Sugarloaf Lodge is an ideal hub for the area's activities. But come back before sunset for the view. Enjoy a glass of local wine and hors d'oeuvres, while you sit and watch the purple shadows lengthen and Allan and Vanessa will advise the best restaurant to suit this special evening. Handy to Auckland for a weekend break with plenty of interesting activities, Sugarloaf offers Bay of Islands bound overseas visitors an excellent introduction to North New Zealand.

Accommodation available (NZ$)	🧍	🧍🧍	+🧍	🛏	🛁	Family dog on site Guest pets by arrangement
2 Suite	$240-270	$240-270	$50	K or 2K		Breakfast: Cooked

Guest rooms:
Ambience:
Setting/location:

LOW   HIG

Property features
Set in 10 acres of isolated bush
Spectacular ocean/beach views
Private track to sandy beaches
Dinghy
TV/DVD/phone/enquire for internet
Potbelly fire
Local features
Natural hot pools/surfing/swimming
Vineyard and wine tasting
Walking tracks/fishing/diving/kayaking
Local restaurant nearby

Bay Lodge

Neil and Carole Wright
Okupu, Great Barrier Island
Tel: 09 4290916
rightway@xtra.co.nz
www.lodgings.co.nz – keyword: baylodge

Auck - 30 mins by air to Claris
Claris - 10 min drive

Hosts can arrange travel. Flight time to Claris airport 30 mins then 10 mins by 4WD to Bay Lodge. Hosts will transfer.

The breathtaking 30-minute scenic flight from Auckland seemed a distant memory as we drove along the private access road towards Bay Lodge. My attention was immediately drawn to the front of the cottage and the spectacular view before me; ten acres of native bush and the deep blue of Okupu Bay below. The music from within welcomed me into the tastefully modernised little cottage. This cottage was indeed perfect for my weekend away from the city; chilled wine in the fridge; flowers and fruit; home-made bread baked daily, and all of my favourite mod cons. I couldn't help but relax. Carole and Neil were there if I needed them, living 100m through the bush, otherwise I was left alone to relax and listen to the waves and tui calling. Access to the beach is by a private track. Guests can fish off the rocks or use the dinghy to catch a snapper or two for dinner, and they can also wander over to the only vineyard on Great Barrier Island, Mellars Boutique Vineyard, for wine tasting. Bay Lodge is perfect for a romantic weekend or as a place to just relax and get back to nature.

Accommodation available (NZ$)	♦	♦♦	+♦	🛏	🛁
1 S/C cottage	$175-250	$175-250		Q	PR

Breakfast: Continental

Guest rooms:
Ambience:
Setting/location:

LOW   HIGH

Supplies stocked by prior arrangement. Enquire for internet & phone access.

39

Bethells Beach Cottages

Trude and John Bethell-Paice
267 Bethells Rd, Waitakere, Auckland
Tel: 09 8109581
Fax: 09 8108677
info@bethellsbeach.com
www.lodgings.co.nz – keyword: bethells

Property features
Health Therapy, Zena Tours
Sunset views over Tasman Sea
Eco friendly and organic produce
Events pavillion/gardens
Table tennis/pentanque/volleyball
Local features
Swimming at Lake Wainamu
Te Henga walkway to Murawai
World class wineries/golf courses
Bethells beach/O'Neills beach
Glow worms/phosphoresence

Waitakere - 15 mins drive
Auckland - 40 mins drive

Take the Lincoln Rd turnoff on
Northwestern motorway turn right on
Universal Dr, follow straight through
Swanson Rd then Scenic Dr, turn off
at Te Henga Rd to Bethells Beach.

Set among giant pohutukawa with panoramic views of Auckland's stunning west coast, Bethells Beach Cottages is a relaxing retreat where you can unwind. The cottages – Te Koinga and Turehu, have private outlooks, barbecues and are fully self-contained. Te Koinga has two bedrooms and is the larger of the two. It's suitable for two couples travelling together but also comfortably accommodates a family. A large private deck set beneath sprawling pohutukawas looks out over the surf crashing on the beach below. It's totally private and outdoor furniture is provided for alfresco dining. Turehu Cottage offers spectacular views of the beach. Bi-folding doors open to a patio area and extensive lawns. Wairua apartment is ideal for a couple with its modern, bright and well appointed furnishings. A summer pavilion accommodates up to 100 people. Trude is also a marriage/civil union celebrant. It is ideal for functions and special occasions. Creativity is encouraged here – having easels and paints available and the lush forest and dramatic coastline has provided inspiration to many artists, poets, writers, singers, musicians and film makers who come to recharge and nourish their creative spirit.

Accommodation available (NZ$)	👤	👤👤	+👤	🛏	🛁	Family cats on site
1 S/C apartment	$281.25	$22.50	Q		PR	Breakfast: Extra $28pp
1 S/C cottage	$331.90	$22.50	Q+Divan		2PR	Evening meal: $35-45pp
1 S/C cottage	$393.75	$33.75	Q+3S+Divan		2PR	Guest rooms:

Studio: internet & phone avail. 2 or 3-course dinner options avail by prior arrangement, min. 6 people. 2 night min stay.

Ambience:
Setting/location:

LOW   HIGH

Property features
English farm atmosphere/tranquility
Dry stone walls/rustic out buildings
Summerhouse/boat shed
Donkey/Llamas/exotic poultry
Large pond/garden walks
Local features
Wineries/restaurants
Four golf courses/quad biking
Horse Riding/Gannet Colony/
Coastal surf beach and Walks
Mineral pools

Willows Reach

Geoff Clarke and Jenny Arscott
252 Boord Cresent, Kumeu, Auckland
Tel: 09 4127004   Mob: 0210341119
Fax: 09 4127059
willowsreach@xtra.co.nz
www.lodgings.co.nz – keyword: willowsreach

Kumeu - 5 mins drive
Auckland - 25 mins drive

From Auckland take the North
western Motorway to join SH16.
At traffic lights at Kumeu turn left
over railway crossing, take 1st left,
Waitakere Rd then next left over
railway crossing Boord Cresent
Willows Reach 1Km on the left.

Head north west from Auckland city just 25 minutes to Kumeu
and so conveniently situated is Willows Reach. Jenny and Geoff have
created this truly amazing haven over a number of years. Entering the
guest room a surprise is in store. This spacious room with its own
deck and even a jetty out over the lake that brushes up to the deck
has a tasteful fishing lodge theme. We were tempted to sit right down
here and watch the bird life, however our hosts who have a grand
sense of humor, tell us there is more so we pour a glass of wine
selected from one of the numerous vineyards this area is renowned
for and wander through the fernery to the summerhouse. The perfect
place to sit, recharge the batteries and contemplate the next few
days. However there is more. We venture further past the stable that
is also home to an array of exotic poultry and llamas down to the boat
house perched on the stream. Geoff tells us this is the place to sit
back, and idle away an hour or so over a malt or two and feel total
peace of mind. Wander back around the lake and there are numerous
pockets of tranquility to take time out. This is the perfect place to
rest up and recover from long flights before heading North to the
Kauri Forests. Many times in our travels the word unique comes up
however Jenny and Geoff's Willows Reach put's new meaning on it.

Family cat/dog on site	Accommodation available (NZ$)					
Breakfast: Special Cooked	1 Room	$375-425	$375-425		Q	EN

Guest rooms:
Ambience:
Setting/location:

Farmstay close to Auckland Room with own decks by the water.

Titirangi Coastal Cottages

Fiona Jeaffreson Mike Reynolds
12 Opou Road, Titirangi, Auckland
Tel: 09 8178323   Mob: 021897731
Fax: 09 8176896
info@coastal-cottages.co.nz
www.lodgings.co.nz – keyword: titirangicoastal

Property features
Sauna/spa/bush walks/native birds
Bush and sea views
Plasma screen/full AV system
Peaceful setting
Local features
Arts and crafts
Cafes and restaurants
Beaches
Monthly Titirangi markets
Art Gallery/theatre
Arataki visitor centre

Titirangi - 3 mins drive
Auckland - 25 mins drive

From city take SH16 west to Great
North Road exit, travel to New Lynn
Continue into Titirangi Rd. Turn left
into Park Rd. Left into Otitori Bay Rd
Left into Opou Rd. Park on platform
– take left stairs to cottage.

The beaches and forest-clad hills of Titirangi comprise a small but growing community only thirty minutes from downtown Auckland. The Coastal Cottage is a hidden gem that is surrounded by native forest yet still has a peep of the sea. It is absolutely private. The only noises I heard for the few days I stayed were from the birds in the trees around. The cottage has two bedrooms, a full kitchen, a huge, open living-area, a sauna and two large decks, one of which has a spa pool. The kitchen, which is bright and cheerful, was equipped with all that I needed, and hosts, Fiona and Mike, had stocked the fridge with a full variety of breakfast foods. This luxurious home away from home has been decorated with modern art and craft, much of it produced by local people. I felt rather spoilt and decided that I could easily have lived at The Coastal Cottage for quite some time. It is only a three-minute drive from the village of Titirangi and I visited the cafes, restaurants and art and craft shops. I was also lucky enough to be there on the last Sunday of the month when the very colourful local market is held.

Accommodation available (NZ$)	👤	👤👤	+👤	🛏	🛁	Guest pets by arrangement
1 S/C house	$450	$450	$30	SK/2S+K	PR	

Breakfast: Special continental
Evening meal: Enquire
Guest rooms:
Ambience:
Setting/location:

LOW   HIGH

Property features
Wrap around sea and city vistas
Exclusive use/fully self-contained
Private spa/sun loungers
BBQ/alfresco dining
Home theatre/multi-room audio
Full office/security/garaging
Local features
Luxury health and beauty spas
Restaurants/cafes/fashion
Sailing/fishing/cruises/ferries
Art galleries/museums/CBD

Viaduct Landing
Essence of New Zealand
Apartment 32, Shed 24, Prince's Wharf,
147 Quay St, Auckland
Tel: 0800377362   Mob: 0275424202
Fax: 09 3582214
stay@essencenz.com
www.lodgings.co.nz – keyword: viaductlanding

Ⓟ 🚶 ✉ 📺 📞

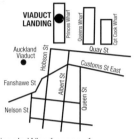

Auckland central
Hamilton - 1 hour drive

Prince's Wharf access from
Hobson St or Quay St. From Nth,
use Fanshawe St exit, From South
exit Nelson St - link into Sturdee
St, then Hobson St. Approach via
Quay St from the East.

Nearby the vibrant cafes and restaurants of the Viaduct Basin in the heart of Auckland, Viaduct landing is an oasis that captures the essence of New Zealand. This elegant, three-bedroom apartment offers guests a luxurious place to stay in one of Auckland's most sought after locations. The apartment is fully self-contained, furnished with every convenience. An extensive collection of the works of New Zealand artists adorn the walls, and a compendium of the work gives information about the artists and the images. Viaduct Landing is surrounded by 200 sq metres of deck and I was captivated by the extensive vistas of city and sea. The simple, clean lines of this architecturally designed building were contrived so that little distracted from the view. I spent the evening wandering around the Viaduct Basin, admiring the yachts and deciding on which of the enticing restaurants I would dine at. It was a very pleasant experience to return to the apartment and sip a wine on the large, all-weather, outdoor area, and then taking a dip in the spa pool which is positioned on the deck to provide sweeping views of the lighted Sky Tower. Viaduct Landing is also a perfect place for corporate functions.

Family cats on site	Accommodation available (NZ$)	🧍	🧍🧍	+🧍	🛏	🛁
Breakfast: Provisions provided	1 S/C suite					
Evening meal: Enquire	High Season	$1350		$169	2SK/T+Q EN+PR	
Guest rooms:	Low Season	$1001		$169		
Ambience:						
Setting/location:	Chef available by prior arrangement. Charges apply. Tariff for up to four people.					

Braemar on Parliament Street

John and Sue Sweetman
7 Parliament Street, Auckland Central
Tel: 09 3775463   Mob: 021640688
Fax: 09 3773056   Free: 0800155463
braemar@aucklandbedandbreakfast.com
www.lodgings.co.nz – keyword: braemar

(P) 👫 ✉ 📺 (C)

Property features
Free broadband
Historic home in Auckland CBD
Local features
High Court - 1 min walk
Old government house - 3 min walk
University of Auckland - 3 min walk
Queen street - 6 min walk
Sky tower - 10 min walk
Parnell shops/cafes - 10 min walk
Museum - 15 min walk
Viaduct Basin bars/restaurants

CBD - 5 mins walk
Parnell - 10 mins walk

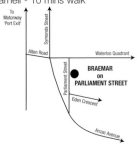

Take 'Port' exit from motorway. At traffic lights take the free left turn up Alten Rd. Turn right at lights into Anzac Ave. Parliament St is the first street on the left, it is opposite the High Court.

Pull up on the leafy surrounds of Parliament Street and you are struck by the contrasts of the 1901 Edwardian architecture that is Braemar on Parliament Street and of the surrounding CBD. In the heart of the city, Braemar is the only historic home that is still an owner occupied residence. Greeted by hosts Susan & John, I was shown to one of two elegant lounges. History abounds here with artworks showing a pictorial record of Auckland's finest old homesteads and landscapes. Another lounge, also beautifully appointed in period furniture, offers all the modern comforts of home, although it is a very short walk to Albert Park and some of Auckland's best cafes and bars. Up the beautiful staircase to the very spacious Batten Suite - a private lounge with sky TV, a fireplace and adjoining bedroom/ensuite. The other two elegant suites share the large bathroom with claw-foot bath and beautiful toiletries. Sumptuous breakfasts are served in the Rose Room. Braemar on Parliament Street is a haven for both corporate travellers and those wanting a peaceful stay in the heart of the city. Susan and John are exceptional hosts and their knowledge of Downtown Auckland history makes Braemar on Parliament Street the perfect place for guests wanting to experience the grandeur that belongs to this era with all the amenities of the CBD.

Accommodation available (NZ$)	👤	👤👤	+👤	🛏	🛁	Family pets on site Guest pets by arrangement
2 Rooms	$180	$205		Q+D	GS	Breakfast: Special cooked
1 Suite	$250	$295	$45	Q	EN	Evening meal: On request
1 Room	$205	$250		Q	PR	Guest rooms:
						Ambience:
Evening meal available by prior arrangement.						Setting/location:

LOW   HIGH

Property features
Guest lounge with fireplace
High speed wireless internet
Guest computer
Laundry facilities/Sky TV/DVD
Local features
Auckland's finest restaurants
Café's/boutique shopping
Harbour/city centre/Sky tower
Gym - 10 mins walk
Parks/galleries/Victoria Park market
Bungy jumping/harbour tours

Amitees on Ponsonby

Ian Stewart Jill Slee
237 Ponsonby Road, Ponsonby, Auckland
Tel: 09 3786325
Fax: 09 3786329
bookings@amitees.co.nz
www.lodgings.co.nz – keyword: amitees

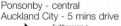

Ponsonby - central
Auckland City - 5 mins drive

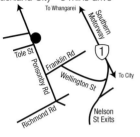

From south take motorway to Nelson St exit. Turn left into Union St & Wellington St, & left into Franklin Rd. Turn right into Ponsonby Rd to Amitees on right. From north take Shelly Beach Rd exit.

This boutique hotel, located in the heart of Auckland's trendy suburb of Ponsonby, has contemporary furnishings and a relaxed casual ambience. The hosts, Jill and Ian, live in their own wing and bestow a friendly welcome to everyone who visits. Guests frequently comment about Jill and Ian's hospitable attention and willingness to share their local knowledge. Ponsonby Road is lined with boutique shops, award-winning cafes and restaurants and is near the city centre and the stunning 'City of Sails' harbour. The luxurious Penthouse suite is located on the upper floor and has a private lounge with spectacular views out to the Sky Tower and the city. The other six guestrooms and the guest lounge are on the ground floor. All have luxury beds, quality cotton linens and robes, Sky TV, DVD players and direct dial phones – making it ideal for both corporate and leisure travellers. The guest lounge has a cosy fireplace, internet service, and a range of magazines and books. A continental breakfast is laid out here for guests to help themselves. From the ground floor I wandered out to a small garden of native grasses and flax bushes - a lovely taste of nature to balance the bustle of the city.

Family cat on site

Breakfast: Continental

Guest rooms:
Ambience:
Setting/location:

Accommodation available (NZ$)	👤	👤👤	+👤	🛏	🛁
1 Room	$180		D		EN
1 Room	$195		2KS		EN
3 Rooms	$235	$35	Q		EN
1 Room	$275	$35	K		EN
1 Room	$400	$35	SK		EN

Warkworth - Matakana - Great Barrier Island - Bethells Beach - Kumeu - Titirangi - Central City - PONSONBY - Remuera - Herne Bay

45

Amerissit Luxury Accommodation

Barbara McKain
20 Buttle Street, Remuera, Auckland
Tel: 09 5229297   Mob: 0272844883
Fax: 09 5229298
barbara@amerissit.co.nz
www.lodgings.co.nz – keyword: amerissit

Property features
Peaceful residential location
Close to city/Newmarket/Remuera
Outdoor areas
Native birds in garden
City circuit bus every 10 mins
Local features
Cafes/restaurants - 10 min walk
Premiere boutique shopping centre
Museum - 20 min walk
Train station - 10 min walk
Auckland Domain - 20 min walk
Newmarket - 1 min drive
Remuera - 1 min drive

From Market Rd Motorway off ramp turn right from South and left from north onto Market Rd. Left into Remuera Rd, at lights right into Bassett Rd. First left into Arney Rd, Buttle St is first right.

This architecturally designed Bed and Breakfast is set in a quiet cul-de-sac in the prestigious residential Auckland suburb of Remuera. The emphasis here is on privacy, peace and tranquillity. Amerissit's minimalist-style suites are designed with executives and the discerning traveller in mind, offering the latest technology: slimline TVs with Sky; DVDs and CDs; in wall or ceiling speakers; direct dial phone and high-speed internet access. The guest rooms are furnished with the finest bed linen, have ensuites and a private balcony or patio. From each room there are views of Remuera, Mt Hobson and the property's surrounding trees and peaceful gardens. Breakfast was a sumptuous affair with a choice of continental or gourmet, served in your room, the dining room, or as I chose, outside on the balcony. Popular with guests visiting Auckland, to explore, to indulge or for a working week – guests from Australia have visited 48 times! This convenient location is only a few minutes by car to the city's popular tourist attractions and the restaurants, bars, cafes, shopping, art galleries, museums, of the Viaduct Harbour, Parnell and Newmarket. Motorway access is nearby. Barbara offers early check-ins for early morning flights and a courtesy-car pickup and drop off service is available if requested.

Accommodation available (NZ$)	🧍	🧍🧍	+🧍	🛏	🛁	
3 Rooms	$150-245	$185-295		K	EN	Breakfast: Special cooked

Guest rooms:
Ambience:
Setting/location:

LOW   HIGH

Property features
Highspeed wireless internet in rooms
LCD TVs/DVD players in rooms/SKY
Friendly flexible hosts
Stylishly renovated villa/sea views
Piano and open fire
Local features
Nearby cafes/restaurants/beaches
Nearby Ponsonby shops
City - 20 mins walk
Beaches short walk
Urban and park walks

Moana Vista

Tim Kennedy Mathew Moran
60 Hamilton Road, Herne Bay, Auckland
Tel: 09 3765028   Mob: 021376150
Fax: 09 3765025   Free: 0800213761
info@moanavista.co.nz
www.lodgings.co.nz – keyword: moanavista

 2

Auckland CBD - 20 mins walk

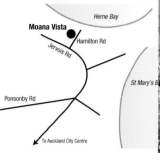

From Auckland head towards Ponsonby up College Hill into Jervois Road. Travel through the Curran Street lights and turn right into Hamilton Road.

The hosts, Tim and Mathew, have renovated and furnished this pretty, two-storeyed villa close to the sea in an inner-city suburb of Auckland. The house was built as a private home in 1896. Now the kitchen, dining room and casual lounge are open plan and adjoining these areas is a larger lounge with an open fireplace, comfortable sofas, a grand piano and state of the art television. My room was downstairs and there are also two upstairs guestrooms opening to a verandah, which overlooks the quiet suburban street and views of the Waitemata Harbour. All are furnished with elegant simplicity in keeping with the style of the house. Breakfast is served in the dining area - a platter of fresh fruit and cereal, baking, coffee and tea. The hosts like the atmosphere to be relaxed and unstructured, so that people can enjoy the friendliness of the place, or keep to themselves if they are seeking solitude. In the evenings many guests like to join Mathew and Tim for a glass of wine on the balcony, or by the fire, before walking to one of the many local cafes for dinner.

Accommodation available (NZ$)	👤	👤👤	+👤	🛏	🛁
1 Room	$140-180	$180-240	$40	Q	EN
1 Room	$140-180	$180-240		Q	EN
1 Room	$140-180	$180-240		Q	PR

Breakfast: Continental

Guest rooms:
Ambience:
Setting/location:

LOW   HIGH

Enquire about low season and long term rates (3+ nights).
Extra bed available on request.

Arthotel The Great Ponsonby

Sally James Gerry Hill
30 Ponsonby Terrace, Ponsonby, Auckland
Tel: 09 3765989
Fax: 09 3765527   Free: 0800766792
info@greatpons.co.nz
www.lodgings.co.nz – keyword: ponsonby

Property features
Free wireless internet
Quiet location no traffic noise
Bicycles/beach towels available
Outdoor courtyards
Close to city
City circuit bus every 10 mins
Local features
Cafes/restaurants - 5 mins walk
Boutique shopping/galleries
Harbour - 20 mins walk
Victoria Park Market
Downtown - 10 mins drive
Airport - 30 mins drive

Ponsonby Tce is at the northern (St Marys Bay) end of Ponsonby Rd. From downtown take Victoria St West, continue past Victoria Market. At top of Hill turn left into Ponsonby Rd. Ponsonby Tce is third on right.

Situated in a quiet street in the middle of a very colourful suburb of Auckland City, this historic eleven room small hotel accommodation displays a very strong sense of place. Its décor reflects its location with a happy blend of Pacific and New Zealand elements - Polynesian masks, tapa cloth, sculptures, ceramics and paintings - and a sunny mix of blue aqua and earth-yellow colours on the walls. Many of these artefacts were bought from the boutique shops of Ponsonby. Within walking distance is, probably, the widest selection of restaurants and cafes in New Zealand. The rooms and suites are spacious, comfortable and bright and a lot of thought has gone into equipping them with almost anything you might need for a stay. I particularly like the sitting room with its comfortable loungers, tea and coffee making facility and loads of books, magazines and CDs, and the adjacent breakfast room which spills out onto a wide verandah. Here the Great Ponsonby's breakfast was served. It was a congenial affair with lots of good-hearted banter between guests and hosts. All the classical dishes are available but I chose one that further enhanced the local flavour – kumera cakes, and grilled fish.

Accommodation available (NZ$)	🧍	🧍🧍	+🧍	🛏	🛁	Family pets on site Guest pets by arrangement
4 Rooms	$220	$220		Q	PR	Breakfast: Special cooked
1 Room	$220	$220		K/T	PR	
1 S/C unit	$245	$245		Q	PR	Guest rooms:
5 S/C units		$245-380		K/T	PR	Ambience:
Seasonal rates apply.						Setting/location:

LOW   HIGH

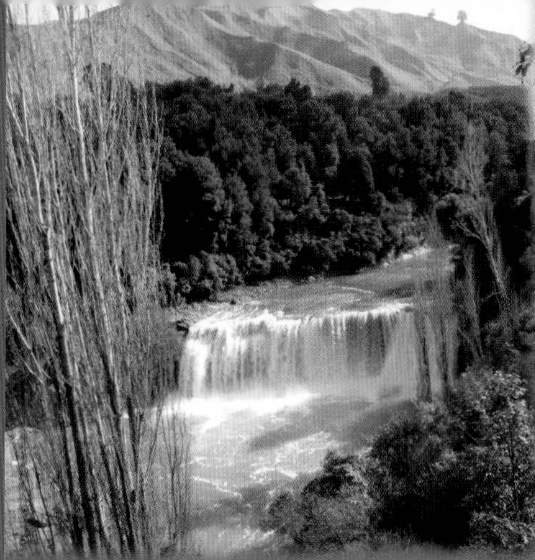

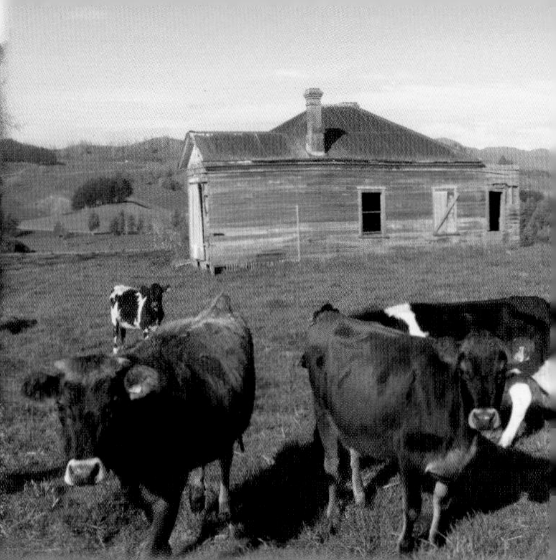

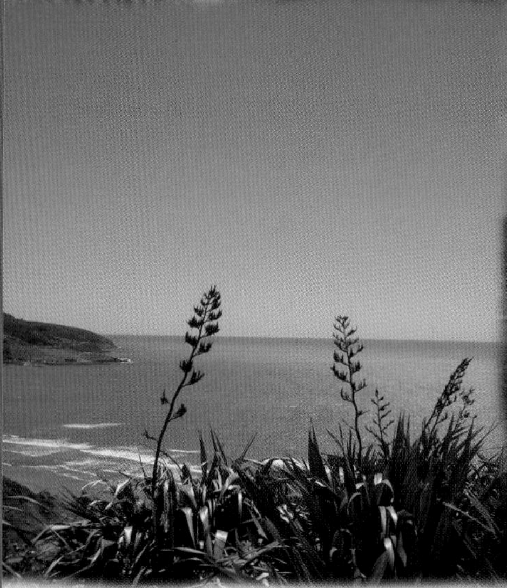

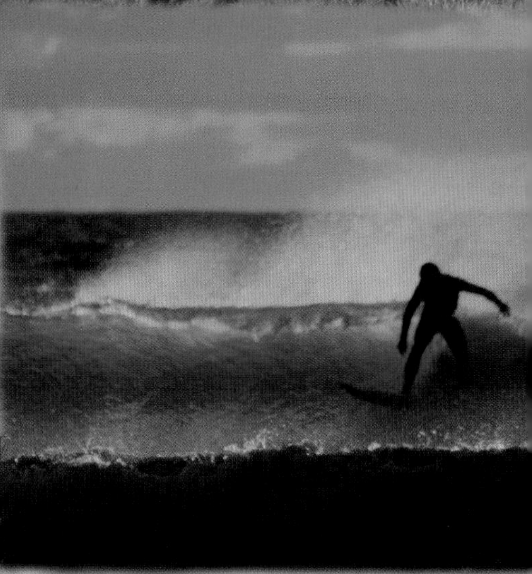

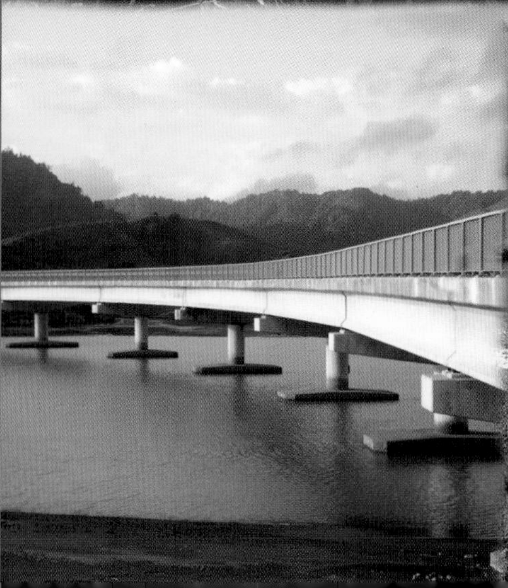

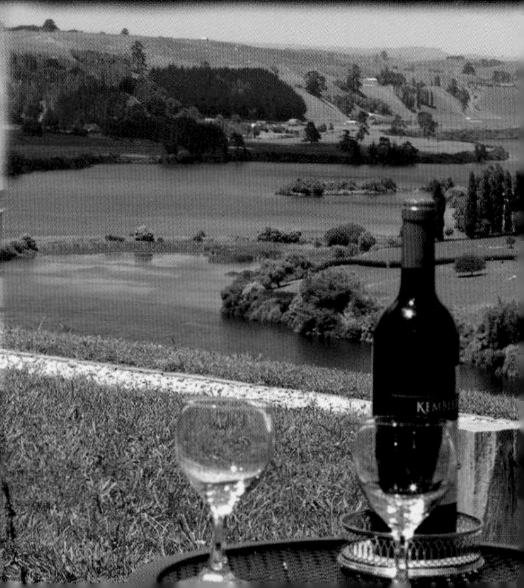

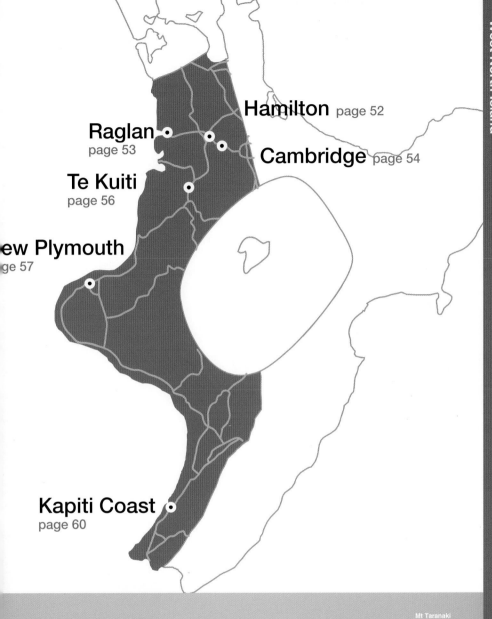

Mt Taranaki

Brooklands Country Estate

General Manager: Marion Jarman
RD 1, Ngaruawahia
Tel: 07 8254756
Fax: 07 8254873
relax@brooklands.net.nz
www.lodgings.co.nz – keyword: brooklands

Property features
5 course meal included in tariff
Tennis court/swimming pool/croquet
Broadband access
Purpose built conference room
Native bush with beautiful bird life
Forest park-10km of walking tracks
Local features
Glow worm caves/golf courses
Waingaro hot springs
Caving/abseiling/flying fox
Raglan village & beaches

Hamilton - 40 mins drive
Auckland - 80 mins drive

Turn off SH 1 at Huntly or
Ngaruawahia and follow signs
to Waingaro Springs (20 mins).
Brooklands is 4km west of
Waingaro Hot Springs.

Four kilometres west of Waingaro Hot Springs, I arrived at one of the original homesteads of this attractive rural area. Brooklands Country Estate has been transformed into a luxury retreat with ten ensuite double bedrooms, which are stylish and contemporary but have kept their homely ambience. Aperitifs and canapés were served on the expansive return verandah overlooking the croquet lawn and the pool. Sometimes they are also served in the outside pavilion, with the stars as company, and on chilly nights, they are enjoyed inside the house around one of the open fireplaces. In the evening, I ate a delightful five-course meal. This was produced by the lodge's renowned chef and served at the large oak table where I sat enjoying the company of other guests. Guests can also choose to dine privately in the library/lounge among candles, chandeliers and crystal. A well-equipped, modern conference room is also available. Groups gather on the wide verandah that overlooks a flood-lit tennis court. This is also an ideal property for small intimate wedding receptions. Often couples have married in the charming, historic St Albans Church, which is 500 metres away from the lodge, and then return to Brooklands to celebrate in the elegant surroundings of this delightful property.

Accommodation available (NZ$)	👤	👤👤	+👤	🛏	🛁	
1 Room	$499	$799		K+S	EN	Breakfast: Special cooked
8 Rooms	$499	$799		K/T	EN	Evening meal: Included
1 Studio	$499	$799		K+Q	EN	Guest rooms:
						Ambience:

Enquire about conference rates and weekend specials.

Setting/location:

LOW   HIGH

Property features
Stunning harbour views
Romantic fireplace
Spectacular sunsets
Expansive sundrenched decks
Local features
Beaches/surf beaches manu bay
Golf courses/habour cruises
Wind/kite surfing/surfing lessons
Swimming bays/boatramp
Cafes/arts & crafts
Scenic walks/fresh seafood

Crabrock House

Rosie and Simon Worsp
24 Rose Street, Raglan
Tel: 07 8254515   Mob: 0272709673
Fax: 07 8254561
rosie.crabrockhouse@xtra.co.nz
www.lodgings.co.nz – keyword: crabrock

Ⓟ 🚶

Raglan - 5 mins walk
Hamilton - 45 mins drive

From Auckland, head south on SH1, turn right at BP Ngaruawahia onto SH39. 17km to SH23 T Junction, turn right. Travel 35km. Drive through main street of Raglan, turn right into Wallis st down to wharf, turn right into Rose St. No 24.

Here's a home with a nautical flavour! Set above Raglans scenic harbour it affords 180 degree views. From the restless Tasman sea, out beyond the heads right around to sheltered upper reaches, it's a feast for the eyes. Décor is carefully shabby/chic in the manner of a traditional Kiwi beach holiday home. This is a place to relax, to soak up that seaside ambience. To watch the trawlers unloading their catch at the fish dock, before wandering down to buy fresh fish for dinner. With three bedrooms and every facility for self catering, Crabrock is very suitable for families, extended stays, girls getaway and boys fishing weekends. Raglan has much to offer. Whilst it's a world recognised surfing venue, there's a raft of activities from caving to abseiling for the vigorous, or join Rosie and Simon at Adventure Waikato. There are bush and shore walks for the less adventurous, and Raglans art galleries, potters and funky shops attract all ages. The perfect end to the days activities, a glass of wine on the deck whilst watching the fishing fleet come to anchor. This really is a seaside holiday.

Guest pets by arrangement	Accommodation available (NZ$)	👤	👥	+👤	🛏	🛁
Breakfast: Enquire	2 Rooms	$180	$250	$25	Q	PR
	1 Room	$180	$250	$25	2S	PR

Guest rooms:
Ambience:
Setting/location:

LOW   HIGH

Local chef for evening meals by prior arrangement

53

The Woolshed

John and Sandra Cottle
625 Scotsman Valley Road, RD 1, Morrinsville 3371
Tel: 07 8240992   Mob: 0275240992
Fax: 07 8240982
thewoolshed@paradise.net.nz
www.lodgings.co.nz – keyword: woolshed

ⓟ ⌨ ✉

MasterCard VISA ♨

Property features
Accom in a converted woolshed
Private deck, garden setting
Farm trips to top of farm
Sky TV/laundry/parking
Local features
Sculpture Park - 5 mins drive
Lake Karapiro - 15 mins drive
Bay of Plenty - 1 hour drive
Raglan beach - 1 hour drive
Waitomo Caves - 1 hour drive
Rotorua - 1 hour drive

Cambridge - 10 mins drive
Hamilton - 20 mins drive

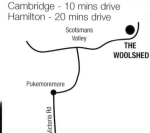

Take SH1 south. Take left at Taupiri.
Follow signs to Cambridge. Follow t
end of Church Rd turn left at sign to
Morrinsville. Take third turn-Hiwi Rd
Follow to T intersection, turn right.
Woolshed 4kms on left.

As I drove the country roads in Central Waikato, I noticed how brilliantly green the rolling pastures were. It was easy to find this converted woolshed, which is located on a 400-acre, working dairy farm. It must be one of the most luxurious woolsheds around. The building has a corrugated-iron roof and plastered exterior walls covered by pretty Virginia vines. Decorative white shutters surround the interior windows allowing the country breezes to flow through the house. Inside, the walls are exposed concrete-block. Flooring is rimu timber and macrocarpa doors separate the guest quarters from the lodge's main living areas. The rooms are decorated with the finest of style and every possible convenience. Sandra is wonderful in the kitchen having previously worked with a top New Zealand celebrity chef. Sandra and John are fabulous and entertaining hosts. After a day exploring the farm, and gourmet dinner, the next day we took the opportunity to join them for a few days at their gorgeous cottage on the Coromandel Peninsula, overlooking the harbour. Both are avid fishermen and lots of friendly rivalry ensured as we battled for the best fish. What a top couple, a top holiday, we will definitely be back. With two choices, this is the ideal location for exploring the Central North Island, The Coromandel and the Bay of Plenty.

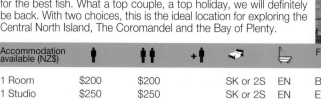

Accommodation available (NZ$)	👤	👥	+👤	🛏	🛁	Family cat on site
1 Room	$200	$200		SK or 2S	EN	Breakfast: Special cooked
1 Studio	$250	$250		SK or 2S	EN	Evening meal: Dinner by request

Guest rooms:
Ambience:
Setting/location:

LOW   HIGH

Evening meal by prior arrangement. Studio has kitchenette & laundry.

Property features
Magnificent lake views
Character home/exquisite décor
Fully landscped gardens
Heated outdoor swimming pool
Spa pool/gym/sauna
Local features
Waitomo caves/Karapiro lake
Rotorua/Mt Maunganui - 45 mins
Cambride Thoroughbred Lodge
Golf courses - 10 to 30 mins
Antique & crafts shops - 15 mins

Emanuels of Lake Karapiro

Ann & Ed Rompelberg
Karapiro Heights, State Highway 1, Waikato
Tel: 07 8237414   Mob: 0274311898
Fax: 07 8237219
info@emanuels.co.nz
www.lodgings.co.nz – keyword: emanuels

Cambridge - 15mins drive
Hamilton - 30mins drive

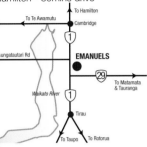

From Cambridge, travel 18km
south on SH1, just before the SH29
intersection to Matamata/Tauranga
you will see Emanuels sign on your
left, opposite the tea rooms. Follow
driveway to the left to top of hill.

Set high on the hills in the heart of Karapiro Heights, you will find this immaculately purpose built home with spectacular views over Lake Karapiro and the surrounding undulating hills. Emanuels was designed and built by the hosts, Ann, Ed and Michael. It was based on a traditional English country style home integrating many local features. They have done an amazing job, with great attention to even the smallest detail. There are 5 luxurious rooms and one suite, each enjoying stunning views with French doors opening out to your very own private patio. The interior design is stunning, from its silk drapes, ornate plaster ceilings, fine cottons, luxurious Italian ensuite with massage shower and much more.   They even have complimentary personalised stationery and postcards. You will receive nothing less than silver service here, the food is fantastic. A drawing room with books, games, self service mini bar, tea and coffee making is available 24 hours. For the more adventurous there is a separate fitness room, spa, sauna, and salt water pool available. The views!!!! The food!!! The great atmosphere!!! Emanuels is the perfect getaway if you want to be spoilt, pampered and enjoy breathtaking views.

Family cat on site

Accommodation available (NZ$)		♦	♦♦	+♦	🛏	🛁
5 Rooms		$350	$400		K or 2S	EN
1 Suite		$800	$850		SK	EN

Breakfast: Cooked
Evening meal: $65pp
Guest rooms:
Ambience:
Setting/location:

LOW   HIGH

55

Tapanui Country Home

Sue and Mark Perry
1714 Oparure Road, RD 5, Te Kuiti
Tel: 07 8778549   Mob: 0274949873
Fax: 07 8778541
info@tapanui.co.nz
www.lodgings.co.nz – keyword: tapanui

Property features
Sheep and cattle farm -1900 acre
Farm tours by arrangement
Peace/tranquility/seclusion
Delicious meals with NZ wine
Romantic getaways
Local features
Waitomo glow-worm cave
Golf courses/horse trekking
Live kiwis/native birds
Black water rafting/The Lost World
Marokopa water fall

Te Kuiti - 20 mins drive
Waitomo - 25 mins drive

From Te Kuiti, take SH3 north for
3km. Turn left into Oparure Road a
continue for 17km. Tapanui Coutnr
Home is on the right, through
limestone entrance.

This really is a rural retreat! Rolling grassland set with high rocky outcrops, dropping away to clusters of bush around clear running streams. Its limestone country, only a few kilometres from Waitomo's famous underground river caves. Set on a 770 hectare sheep and cattle farm, Tapanui Country Home is guarded by magnificent rock pillars clearly visible from the road. Travellers may stay at the Country Home, or choose a self contained cottage, half a kilometre or so across the farm. This is no shepherds hut. Furnished and outfitted to a high standard the accommodation will suit the discerning traveller. It affords an excellent insight into New Zealand broken country farming, in comfort and style. Have you ever driven rural roads and wondered how life is on these remote farms? Tapanui is a working farm. It's huge, and within the constraints of safety, it is Sue and Mark's delight to acquaint guests with the day to day routines such property imposes. "There are some stunning walks", says Sue "My preference is to four-wheel drive my guests around the farm for orientation and explanations and after that they can choose to stroll back, if that's their wish". No, this isn't a farm stay, it is a mix of farm and rural retreat with most delightful scenery, a photographers' delight.

Accommodation available (NZ$)	👤	👤👤	+👤	🛏	🛁	Family cat on site
1 Suite	$200	$250		SK/T	EN	Breakfast: Cooked
1 S/C house	$200	$250	$60	SK/T + Q	PR	Evening meal: $60pp
						Guest rooms:
						Ambience:

Iron and ironing board available upon request..

Setting/location:

Property features
Stunning views of Mt Egmont
1900's villa style home
Guest lounge with open fire
Courtesy pick up
Beautiful gardens
Local features
Swimming/surfing beaches
Coastal walkways/bushwalks
18 hole golf course
Restaruants/cafes/bars
Egmont National Park

New Plymouth - 15 mins drive
Inglewood - 15 mins drive

North from Wellington, turn left at
Inglewood to SH3 towards New
Plymouth. Travel 4km turn right into
Upland Road. From North take the
3A road to Inglewood, Whanganui.

Villa Heights Bed and Breakfast
John and Rosemary Lucas
333 Upland Road, RD 2 New Plymouth
Tel: 06 7552273   Mob: 0274164131
villaheights@xtra.co.nz
www.lodgings.co.nz – keyword: villaheights

Retired farmers Rosemary and John consider their near lifetime association with the land well qualify them as hosts. "But the farmhouse wasn't suitable, so we restored this". Their gracious Victorian villa is an absolute delight. Set in beautiful formal gardens, behind a sweeping drive, the villa is unpretentious to the arriving traveller. Delight awaits those who appreciate finely crafted timbers. This is not the dark wood panelling of an Irish country home or English gentleman's club. Panels and ceilings are of rich, glowing New Zealand natives. It is the product of modern craftsmanship and the result is spectacular. Pointing to the ornately crafted timber ceiling John explains the enormity of the work. However this home is not just about the house and its spectacular views, it also about the wonderful warm hospitality that we experienced. Rosemary and John are well qualified to advise you on the many attractions of Taranaki, including the gardens – a great passion of theirs. There are also the beaches and the beautiful countryside. Stay here for Irish-Kiwi hospitality, for the most wonderful timber work and for those views of the mountain.

Guest pets by arrangement	Accommodation available (NZ$)	🧍	🧍🧍	+🧍	🛏	🛁
Breakfast: Cooked	1 Room		$140-160		K	EN
Evening meal: $35pp	2 Rooms	$110	$130-160	$45	2Q	EN
Guest rooms:						
Ambience:						
Setting/location:						

LOW   HIGH

Iron, laundry and internet available on request.

Nice Hotel and Bistro

Terry Parkes
71 Brougham Street, New Plymouth
Tel: 06 7586423   Mob: 0274576633
Fax: 06 7586433
info@nicehotel.co.nz
www.lodgings.co.nz – keyword: nicehotel

(P) ✉ 📺 ✆ ♿

💳 💳 💳 VISA

Property features
Award winning bistro
Deck/tropical garden
Contemporary NZ art/bikes
Jetstream/business centre
Meeting room/weddings/functions
Local features
Pukekura Park/Pukeariki museum
Walk to contemporary art museum
Historic St Mary's Church
Len Lye Wind Wand
Coastal walkway

New Plymouth - 1 min walk
Hamilton - 2 hour drive

Devon St
Powderham St
Broughman St — NICE HOTEL & BISTRO — Liardet St — Gover St
Vivian St

Entering into New Plymouth stay or
the main Northgate Rd follow to the
lights by the fire station. Nice Hotel
is across the viaduct on the right
diagonally across from St Mary's.

    Located in New Plymouth's city centre, Nice Hotel & Bistro
is the only luxury boutique hotel in town. The hotel boasts
chandeliers and rich-coloured halls lined with contemporary New
Zealand artworks. It has seven large, bright, airy guestrooms
which have ensuites with double spa baths or massage showers.
All guestrooms have their individual charm, each named and
decorated after an element of New Plymouth's history – the
Redcoats room, the Pukeariki room or the Windwand room.
Within walking distance of numerous tourist sites, the hotel's
location also caters for business travellers. Each room has a large
desk and broadband internet connection. Terry has developed the
nooks and crannies of this 140 year-old New Plymouth residence.
I relaxed, for instance, in an alcove found on the second floor
where there was a small library, plush armchairs and the sound of
classical music. The on-site award winning Bistro has an a-la-carte
menu catering for in-house guests during the day, and open to the
public for dinner. Outside, a large deck, surrounded by a tropical
garden, is an oasis in this central city location. By day the Nice
Hotel & Bistro is run with slick and professional service but when
the sun goes down the ambience is more romantic in style.

Accommodation available (NZ$)	🧍	🧍🧍	+🧍	🛏	🛁	Family dog on site Guest pets by arrangement
5 rooms	$225	$225	Q	EN		Breakfast: Extra $15pp
2 Rooms	$225	$225	SK	EN		Evening meal: Menu
1 Suite	$333	$333	SK	EN		Guest rooms:
						Ambience:
Ensuites have massage showers or spa baths.						Setting/location:

LOW   HIC

Property features
Inner city tranquility
Unique architecture & contemp décor
Separate guest lounge & S/C kitchen
Designer ensuites - 2 spa baths
Guest deck & bbq with bush outlook

Local features
Pukeariki & costal walkway - 5 mins
Pukekura Park - 2 mins
Surf beach/golf courses
Cafes/restaurants - walking distance
Art gallery - 5 mins

Wanganui - 2 hours drive
Hamilton - 2 hours 30 mins drive

Driving from North turn left into Liardet St at traffic lights, first right to Pendarves St and you will see Issey Manor to your left.

Issey Manor
Jan and Brian Mason
32 Carrington Street, New Plymouth
Tel: 06 7582375   Mob: 0272486686
Fax: 06 7582375
issey.manor@actrix.co.nz
www.lodgings.co.nz – keyword: isseymanor

(P) 👥 ✉ 📺 (C)   MasterCard VISA

Issey Manor is a combination of historical architecture and modern living and suits both corporate and leisure travellers visiting New Plymouth. Painted orange and brown on the outside, this stylish urban bed and breakfast began life as a coach-house in 1857. The guestrooms are all spacious, styled in bright colours and contemporary furnishings with outlooks to the surrounding rooftops and trees of the residential neighbourhood. Contemporary New Zealand artwork is displayed throughout and a private guest lounge has a well-stocked library, with Sky television, DVD player and stereo. Jan and Brian serve breakfast and guests are welcome to use the fully equipped, modern guest kitchen throughout the day and evening. Although Jan and Brian live on-site, I was amazed at how much privacy I had; the main portico entrance and private locations of the four guestrooms allow guests to come and go undisturbed. That afternoon after exploring the numerous sights of New Plymouth I discovered a large deck area hidden at the rear of the property that looked out to a small valley lined with native trees – a great place to unwind. I thought the table and chairs and barbecue would be perfect for alfresco dining on a summer evening.

Family pets on site

Breakfast: Special cooked

Guest rooms:
Ambience:
Setting/location:

Accommodation available (NZ$)	👤	👥	+👤	🛏	🛁
1 Room	$140	$170	$45	SK or 2S	EN
1 Room	$130	$150		Q	EN
1 Room	$120	$140		Q	EN
1 Room	$120	$140		Q	EN

Te Horo Lodge

Craig Garner
109 Arcus Road, Te Horo, Kapiti Coast
Tel: 06 3643393   Mob: 0274306009
Fax: 06 3643323   Free: 0800483467
enquiries@tehorolodge.co.nz
www.lodgings.co.nz – keyword: tehoro

Property features
Swimming pool/spa pool
Petanque court/2 hectares bush
Small conference room (holds 12)
Tranquil setting/open fire
Rural/garden views/olive grove
Local features
Southward car museum - 20 mins
5 golf courses - 30 mins
Ruth Pretty Cooking School
Kapiti Island excursions - 25 mins
Kapiti 4x4 quad bike - 30 mins

Wellington - 50 mins drive
Levin - 20 mins drive

Approx. 8km south of Otaki, turn o
SH 1 opposite the Red House Cafe
onto School Rd. Turn left onto Arc
Rd. Lodge is number 109.

The drive into Te Horo Lodge winds through a stand of native kohekohe trees before opening out into a courtyard and the entrance to this impressive purpose-built accommodation. In this fertile pocket of land close to the Otaki River, Craig has built an elegant cedar building against a backdrop of native bush and a sheltered, two-and-a-half acre lawn brightened with flower gardens and an orchard of citrus, kiwi fruit and stone fruit beyond. The result is a place that has two great luxuries: the peace and the view. I imagined myself breakfasting in the gazebo by the outdoor pool or relaxing in the jacuzzi under the stars. In the lodge's interior Craig has combined timber shutters and frames with fruity-coloured walls bright curtaining and a tiled floor. The result is chic and sophisticated without being the least bit pretentious. The ensuite bedrooms are understated and cheerfully coloured, with glass doors that lead to the garden. My upstairs suite featured a large round window looking right into the treetops and the serenity of the forest. There is a small conference room, but the most charming room in the house is the lounge with its dominant stone chimney which is a work of art that has been crafted by a local stone mason.

Accommodation available (NZ$)	👤	👤👤	+👤	🛏	🛁	
3 Rooms	$160-180	$215-305		SK	EN	Breakfast: Cooked
1 Room	$180-230	$265-350	$85	SK+S	EN	Evening meal: $50-65pp

Guest rooms:
Ambience:
Setting/location:

Evening meals by prior arrangement.

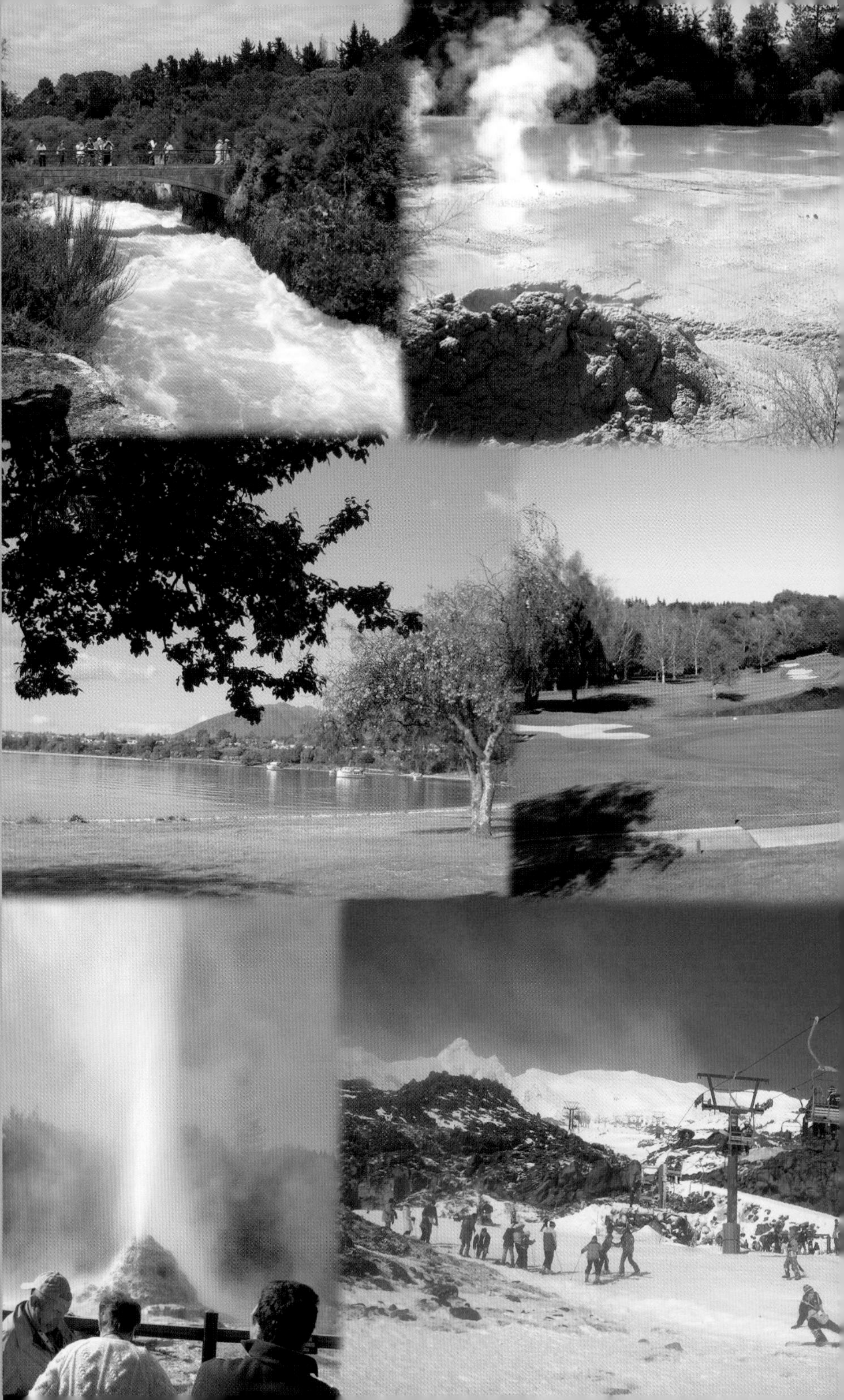

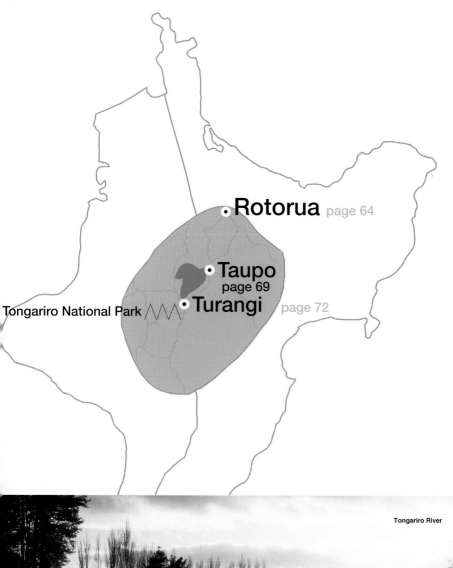

Tongariro National Park /\\/\\/\\

Tongariro River

Springwaters Lodge

Steve and Katherine Whyte
9 Te Waerenga Road, Hamurana, Rotorua
Tel: 07 3322565   Mob: 0212953652
info@springwaterslodge.co.nz
www.lodgings.co.nz – keyword: springwaterslodge

qualmark
★★★★
guest & hosted

Property features
Spa/laundry/underfloor heating
En suited rooms/robes/safes
Wireless broadband
Views of lake
TV and DVD in all rooms
Local features
9 hole Golf course - 500 m
Hamurana Springs - 500 m
Playground - 1 km
Local fly fishing & trolling tours
birdwatching/tourist attractions

Rotorua - 12 mins drive
Tauranga - 45 mins drive

From Rotorua town centre, follow
SH6 towards Ngongotaha for 9.5k
passing Ngongotaha and Hamuran
Continue pass the golf course, turn
left into Te Waerenga Road, look c
for the horse letter box.

Tucked into Lake Rotorua's north western shore, across from the cities blaze of night light, there's Springwaters Lodge. This modern purpose built facility gets its name from Hamurana Springs, flowing into the lake alongside the lodge. Steve and Katherine, both with a hospitality and tourism background, have set about to provide a true taste of Kiwiana. Steve, who demonstrates sheep shearing and livestock handling at the nearby Agrodome says, "Tourists, especially families, really appreciate personal involvement." Especially welcome are children of all ages, as they regard guest interaction with their own children, a bonus. Rotorua's tourist activities are legendry, but maybe a time out day at the lodge appeals. There's Hamurana Springs and Redwood forest to explore. There's trout fishing on the lake in front of the lodge. What about a casual game of golf? Steve has a few sets of clubs and there is a nice nine holes next door. Lodge décor is crisply modern to a high standard decorated with fascinating kiwi memorabilia and local art. Stay here to escape Rotorua's tourist strip, and to experience the flavour of New Zealand life with the accent on family.

Accommodation available (NZ$)	👤	👥	+👤	🛏	🛁	Guest pets by arrangement
2 Rooms	$180	$200	SK or T	EN		Breakfast: Cooked
1 Room	$150	$180	K	EN		Evening meal: $60pp
1 Room	$150	$180	SK	EN		Guest rooms:
						Ambience:
Iron, complimentary snacks, refreshments, spa and games available.						Setting/location:

RECOMMENDED
★★★★
BOUTIQUE
LODGINGS

LOW   H

Property features
Private beach
Gymnasium
Tennis court
Massage therapy room
Billiard room

Local features
Maori culture
Geothermal wonders
Lakes/fishing
Numerous tourist attractions

Peppers On The Point - Lake Rotorua

David Smail
214 Kawaha Point Road, Kawaha Point, Rotorua
Tel: 07 3484868   Mob: 0272451101
Fax: 07 3481868
onthepoint@peppers.co.nz
www.lodgings.co.nz – keyword: onthepoint

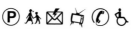

Rotorua - 10 mins drive
Auckland - 3 hour drive

From Fairy Springs Rd, turn into Kawaha Point Rd. Follow the brown signs saying lodges, we are number 214, at the very end. If the gate is closed ring the bell, drive in to the front of the house.

A short ten-minute drive from Rotorua, Peppers on the Point is luxurious accommodation with panoramic views over Lake Rotorua to Mokoia Island. I had the choice of staying in the Lake Cottage Suite, with a large deck and open-air spa bath; the Lake Villa, a four-bedroom home with extensive lake views; or one of the classic suites. I decided on one of the spacious classic suites, enticed by its large ensuite and spa bath and seeing myself enjoying a book and relaxing in the lovely surrounds. After settling in, I walked along the track, which winds through the native forest on the property and then headed for the private beach. Back at the lodge, I was tempted to indulge in a massage and beauty treatment in the on-site therapy room, but decided instead to relax on the deck in the sun. Dinner, prepared by the resident chef, was a good example of beautifully presented, New Zealand cuisine. From the underground cellar, where a wide range of the best New Zealand wines is stored, I selected my own bottle of wine. Peppers on the Point is a memorable retreat with everything guests need to celebrate of the good things of life.

Family cat on site
Guest pets by arrangement

Breakfast: Cooked
Evening Meal: Available
Guest rooms:
Ambience:
Setting/location:

Accommodation available (NZ$)	🧍	🧍🧍	+🧍	🛏	🛁
1 Suite	$1109	$1392	$300 SK/T		EN
6 Suites	$932	$1156	$300 SK/T		EN
2 Cottages	$932	$1156	$300 SK/T		EN
1 Lake Villa	$2812.50	$2812.50			PR

Lake Villa is priced for whole house (4 bedrooms, 2 bathrooms), B&B only.

Villa Florrie

Fraser Family
7 Alexander Road, Lake Tarawera
Tel: 04 5686819   Mob: 021468923
Fax: 04 5686342   Free:
raewyn@fraser.org.nz
www.lodgings.co.nz – keyword: villaflorrie

Property features
Luxury lake edge villa
Flat lawn to lake edge/private jetty
Landscaped parklike surroundings
Lagoon views from lakeside rooms
7m luxury pontoon boat avail.
Local features
Trophy trout fishing
Boating/lake cruising
Thermal attractions/natural hot pools
Landing Café licensed café
Buried village

Rotorua - 20 mins drive
Tauranga - 60 mins drive

Turn off SH33 onto Tarawera Rd. Pas
the blue & green lakes, and the Burie
Village. At the Tarawera Landing
turnoff, continue into Spencer Rd. Tra
7 km – Alexander Rd is on your right
Villa Florrie is at the bottom of the hill.

Travel along the picturesque Spencer Road as it winds along the edge of beautiful Lake Tarawera and right at the end you will find Villa Florrie, a luxury self contained lake front villa on the edge of Otumutu Lagoon. Secluded from the world, the grounds are park like with a gentle slope down to the lake edge and private jetty. Stepping inside the interior is spacious, furnished in a comfortable contemporary style and decorated with examples of Maori and Pacific art. It's all here, TV, DVD, Sky TV, selection of DVDs, books, magazines. All lakeside rooms have doors opening to extensive deck areas that are set up for entertainment, rain or shine. Even from my bed I could see, across the lawn to the jetty and lake edge where ducks and swans were gliding through the water. The sound of native Tui replaced that of the Moreporks (small New Zealand owls). All the activities this area is famous for are nearby, such as trophy trout fishing, thermal attractions, hot pools, bush walks, and cultural activities however I found this a great place to relax for a few days flyfishing, swimming from the jetty and just sitting with a drink admiring the view. It was all too good to leave. As a memento I purchased one of their beautifully crafted Tuatara's which was packed in a special gift box for my journey.

Accommodation available (NZ$)	👤	👤👤	+👤	🛏	🛁
1 S/C house (4 bedrooms)	$650-800	$80	3Q + 2S	2 GS	

Breakfast: Not available

Guest rooms:
Ambience:
Setting/location:

3rd bedroom has kitchenette and fireplace. 4th bedroom has 2 singles.

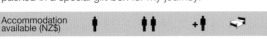

Property features
Swim, fish & boat from own jetty
Private bushwalk & birdwatching
Sun facing view of tranquil lagoon
Petanque & picnic on lawn
Local features
Guided trout fishing
Scenic/fishing helitours
Scenic floatplane tours
Jet-skiing/natural hot pools
Hiking trails/volcanic tours
Buried Village/cultural experiences

Pukeko Landing
Essence of New Zealand
6 Ronald Road, Lake Tarawera, Rotorua
Tel: 0800377362   Mob: 0275424202
Fax: 09 3582214
stay@essencenz.com
www.lodgings.co.nz – keyword: pukekolanding

Ⓟ 🚶 ✉ 📺 📞

Rotorua - 15 mins drive
Taupo - 1 hour drive

From SH33 (Te Ngae Rd) turn into
Tarawera Rd. After approx 13 km's
continue straight ahead into Spencer
Rd. Travel another 7 km's to Ronald
Rd on your right. Pukeko Landing is
300m on the left.

As the road meandered closer to Pukeko Landing, I managed to catch a glimpse of beautiful Lake Tarawera between the hedgerows. Once there, I never wanted to leave! I enjoyed dining on the deck in the evening, looking across the water, listening to the surrounding bird song. The step down deck area with a large extendable umbrella is perfect any time of day. From the house, guests can wander down the landscaped path to the water's edge and relax on the private jetty sipping a cool drink or play a game of petanque on the lawn. Clearwater Charter Boats are nearby for organising lazy days on the lake, trips to the thermal springs, or fishing, water skiing and wet biking for the more adventurous. This well appointed three-bedroom lakeside cottage is perfect for a couple, a family or group of friends. Although the open plan kitchen, dining and indoor/outdoor living encourages gatherings, the bedrooms are private and chic. I must mention how I soaked in the master bedroom ensuite's bath, gazing out to the expanse of the lagoon. I had a truly memorable stay at this special place in a delightful and typically New Zealand environment.

Accommodation available (NZ$)	👤	👥	+👤	🛏	🛁
1 S/C house					
High Season	$1226	$169	2SK/2S	EN	
Low Season	$889	$169	+2S	+PR	

Breakfast: Provisions provided
Evening meal: Enquire
Guest rooms:
Ambience:
Setting/location:

Chef available by prior arrangement. Charges apply. Tariff is for up to 4 people.

67

The Pheasant Cottage at Treetops

Heiko Kaiser
351 Kearoa Road, RD 1, Rotorua
Tel: 07 3332066
Fax: 07 3332065
info@treetops.co.nz
www.lodgings.co.nz – keyword: treetops

(P) 🚶 ✉ 📺 (C)

💳 💳 💳 **VISA** 💳

Property features
2500 acres of native forestry
Horse riding and fishing on site
Mountain bikes/kayaks available
70km hiking trails
Fine local cusine
Fully furnished cottage
Local features
Rotorua-central of Maori culture
Geysers and Buried Village
Scenic fights/helitours
Boat charters

Rotorua - 25 mins drive
Taupo - 45 mins drive

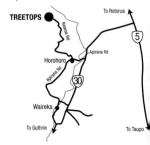

From Rotoura/Taupo, turn onto SH
travel 10km, take the first road on th
right, signposted to Treetops contin
on to Kearoa Road travel 3km to en
of the road, go through the gates ar
travel 2.5km to Treetops.

Hidden in the hills behind Rotorua, just 25 minutes from the town, The Pheasant Cottage at Treetops Estate is the perfect getaway. Located in the heart of New Zealand's famous therapeutic thermal region, the cottage is perfectly situated at the east end of this property, which has 2500 acres of native forest. Treetops is a carefully managed game and wildlife habitat featuring trout streams, lakes, waterfall, hiking and mountain bike trails. You can enjoy the splendour of this natural setting and on my first day I did just that while sipping a drink on the deck; the perfect end to the day. The cottage's three luxurious style bedrooms can sleep up to eight guests sharing two bathrooms. Its fully-equipped kitchen is ideal for those wanting the flexibility of self catering, however, guests also have the choice of dining at the world renowned Treetops Lodge just a short distance away. Nothing is too much trouble for the wonderful staff there. They are happy to arrange an unparalleled range of activities and exhilarating experiences from your doorstep. The cottage is the perfect place from which families or couples can experience this wonderful sanctuary.

Accommodation available (NZ$)	👤	👥	+👤	🛏	🛁	Guest pets by arrangement
1 S/C cottage	$450-600	$200-300	K		EN	Breakfast: By arrangement
			K or 2S		PR	

Guest rooms:
Ambience:
Setting/location:

Rate 3 - 4 persons $750-900. Evening meal by arrangement at Treetops Lodge.

LOW   HIG

Property features
Beautiful lanscaped gardens
Grass tennis court
River walks
Complete privacy
Laundry/International wine selection
Local features
Lake activities/jet boats
Huka Falls
Numerous fishing spots
International golf courses
Skifields - 1 hour

Taupo Garden Lodge
William and Suzanne Hindmarsh
70 Hindmarsh Drive, Taupo 3352
Tel: 07 3789847   Mob: 0275531253
Fax: 07 3785799   Free: 0800426538
www.lodgings.co.nz – keyword: taupogarden

Taupo - 5 mins drive
Rotorua - 45 mins drive

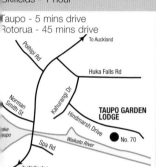

From north of Taupo, on SH1,
turn into Huka Falls road, then
into Kahurangi Drive, then left into
Hindmarsh Drive. Taupo Garden
Lodge is down on the right, no 70.

Pulling up at the elegant wrought iron gates and you know that you are going to be welcomed to a very special place. William and Suzanne have established this extraordinary haven on the banks of the Waikato River where it bursts from Lake Taupo and surges down the wonderful Huka Falls and finally out to sea. This fishing lodge with two suites – The Garden and The Heron – are adorned with Persian rugs and interesting artworks. So close to town but so private, I walked with Suzanne through the gardens. This place is not called 'Garden Lodge' on a whim. Magnificent rhododendrons, camellia, roses and perennials all painting an enduring picture and Suzanne knows the botanical names of every one – amazing! They have lovingly created these gardens over many years. We join William and Suzanne in the garden beside the lily pond for a glass of wine from William's highly acclaimed wine cellar before heading into town to one of the recommended restaurants. They could have been a world away – not five minutes. This is the perfect place to stay a few days, take in the world renowned golf courses, fish Lake Taupo and rivers or head to the central plateau for skiing or tramping. Guests are very important to your hosts who will join you for breakfast and will happily help to plan your day.

Labrador dog on site

	Accommodation available (NZ$)	🧍	🧍🧍	+🧍	🛏	🛁
Breakfast: Cooked	1 Suite	$400	$60	K+S	EN	
Evening meal: $85pp	1 Suite	$400	$60	Q+S	EN	
Guest rooms:	(2 nights)	$650				
Ambience:	(3 nights)	$975				
Setting/location:						

LOW   HIGH

Te Kowhai Landing

Essence of New Zealand
325 Lake Terrace, 2 Mile Bay, Taupo
Tel: 0800377632   Mob: 0275424202
Fax: 09 3582214
stay@essencenz.com
www.lodgings.co.nz – keyword: tekowhailanding

(P) 🚶 ✉ 📺 (📞)

💳 MasterCard VISA 🙂

Property features
Full gourmet kitchen & alfresco dining
Dual living spaces, feature fireplaces
NZ contemporary art & sculpture
Spa pool/lake edge swimming
Row-boat/petanque/fly fishing
Lake views from every room
Local features
Guided trout fishing & hunting
International golf course
Water pursuits/aerial adventures
Restaurants/wine-tasting

Taupo - 35 mins walk/5 min drive
Rotorua - 45 mins drive

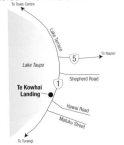

Te Kowhai landing is between the lake edge and State Highway 1 at 2 Mile Bay, just north of the 'Sail Centre'.

Approaching Te Kowhai Landing, which sits on the waters edge of Lake Taupo, I could not miss the striking road frontage that offers a barrier from the bustle of the road to the private haven within. Large entrance doors unveiled magnificent and intimate water views, through full-length double-glazed doors and windows. From here you either step upstairs where a bridge links two exclusive suites or down to the ground floor living that includes two separate living areas both with a fireplace, a full gourmet kitchen and indoor and outdoor dining spaces, or have Te Kowhai's manager Nicky, a fully trained chef, prepare a gourmet dinner for you. The cosy underfloor heating was welcoming on a cool autumn day. Enjoy the naturally inspired outdoor heated soak pool where you can listen to the water lapping and then cool off in the lake. The style and design detail of this purpose-built, self-contained lodge is exceptional and reminiscent of a typical New Zealand boatshed. Details include state-of-the-art wiring, which provides communications and conveniences with finger tip control. Stylish shops and restaurants are only a five-minute drive or 35-minute lake edge walk away. This is a wonderful base to access all that the Central Plateau of the North Island region has to offer.

Accommodation available (NZ$)	🧍	🧍🧍	+🧍	🛏	🛁
1 S/C house					
High Season	$1350	$169	2SK/Twin	2EN	
Low Season	$1001	$169	2S in living	+ 1PR room	

Chef available by prior arrangement. Charges apply. Tariff is for up to 4 people.

Breakfast: Provisions provided
Evening meal: Enquire
Guest rooms:
Ambience:
Setting/location:

LOW   HK

Property features
Swimming pool/tennis court
Conservatory and courtyard
Three acres of garden
Petanque
Gazebo and pond
Separate guest lounge/dining
Complimentary laundry service

Local features
Lake activities/jet boats
Golf/hot pools/bungy jumping
Trout fishing

Taupo - 10 mins drive
Rotorua - 1 hour drive

The Pillars

Ruth and John Boddy
7 Deborah Rise, Bonshaw Park, Taupo
Tel: 07 3781512
Fax: 07 3781511   Free: 0800200983
info@pillars.co.nz
www.lodgings.co.nz – keyword: pillars

 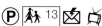 13

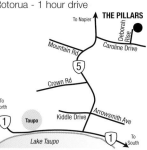

To Napier **THE PILLARS**
Deborah Rise
Caroline Drive
Mountain Rd
5
Crown Rd
To North
1 Taupo Kiddle Drive Arrowsmith Ave
Lake Taupo
1 To South

South of Taupo township take SH 5
towards Napier. Drive approx. 6 kms
and turn right into Caroline Drive.
Turn left into Deborah Rise, The
Pillars is on your right.

This modern country manor sits on five acres of park-like grounds with a rural view extending to the lake and mountains. There is also a lot of space in the house, a spacious lounge and conservatory, a large expanse of verandah and courtyard areas and guestrooms ranging from comfortable to huge. The décor is described as classical but certainly not so formal as to compromise comfort and relaxation. I stayed in the largest room which is very convenient for a long stay (but still delightful for just one night) with furniture such as a desk, lounge chair and couch, television and a huge ensuite bathroom with a dressing alcove. Ruth and John go the extra mile. Little extras like writing paper, herbal teas and plunger coffee, cookies, fruit, a choice of beverages and a complimentary bottle of wine in the room. As a guest I wanted for nothing. Taupo is just a short drive away but, like most people, I settled down here to take advantage of this mini-resort, which has a tennis court, swimming pool and large established gardens to wander through. An excellent breakfast was served in the dining room that looks out to the sunny and lavender-lined courtyard.

Family cats on site

Breakfast: Special continental
Evening meal: $65pp
Guest rooms:
Ambience:
Setting/location:

LOW   HIGH

Accommodation available (NZ$)	👤	👥	+👤	🛏	🛁
1 Room			$290	SK/T	EN
1 Room			$290	K/T	EN
1 Room			$390	CK/T	EN
1 Room			$490	CK/T	EN

Off-season discounts available. Large expansive property with 3 acre garden, tennis court and pool.

Waimarama Fishing Lodge

Graeme Knapp
4 Kokopu Street, Turangi
Tel: 06 3579552
waimarama.fishinglodge@xtra.co.nz
www.lodgings.co.nz – keyword: waimarama

Property features
Riverside location
Spacious grounds with mature trees
Central heating/open fire
Sky TV/DVD/sound system
Well equipped kitchen/library
Local features
Tongariro River - 2 mins walk
Mount Ruapehu/The Chateau
18 hole golf course - 5 mins drive
Hiking/mountain biking
Thermal pools/Lake Taupo/boat ramp

Turangi - 2 mins drive
Taupo - 40 mins drive

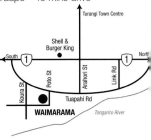

Turn into Arahori St opposite Shell/
Burger King, turn right into Taupahi
Rd. Turn left into Poto St. The
lodge is on the corner of Poto and
Kokopu Streets.

This self-catered lodge could not be closer to the world famous Tongariro River. The famous Major Jones Fishing Pool is a stones throw away directly across the road. Waimarama Fishing Lodge provides luxury accommodation for up to eight people in both the main house and the romantic cottage in the garden. All guest rooms are beautifully furnished with the finest linens, goose down duvets, the master room has all the wow factor with full ensuite marble bathroom. The showers rate a special mention. Piping hot water cascades from overhead, reminiscent of standing under a waterfall – fantastic! It was not long before we settled in with the complimentary bottle of wine in front of the glorious open fire that had been lit for us. The fully equipped kitchen is a chef's paradise. However it is the library that holds our fascination, full of historic books collected over many years by the homes first owner, Dr Ron Kennedy. Our fishing guide was there to greet us at dawn and soon we were flicking our lines, attempting to drop the flies in the right place. Waimarama Fishing Lodge is not all about fishing however and we spent the next few days hiking, mountain biking in the Tongariro National Park and relaxing with a book in the garden. It really was worth the journey to call Waimarama Lodge ours for a few days.

Accommodation available (NZ$)					
1 S/C house	$300	$50	2Q + 2S	EN, GS	Breakfast: Not available

A S/C cottage is also available & can only be rented with the house.
The house & cottage can cater for a maximum of 8 guests.

Guest rooms:
Ambience:
Setting/location:

LOW   HIG

Cathedral Cove

Courtesy of Gull Cottage

The Heights Bed and Breakfast

Vicky and Phil English
300 Grafton Road, Thames
Tel: 07 8689925   Mob: 0211509642
Free: 0800689925
info@theheights.co.nz
www.lodgings.co.nz – keyword: theheights

Property features
Panoramic sea views
Spacious rooms w/ensuite
Private patio/deck
Tranquil, park like garden
Local features
Beaches
Historic gold mine museum
Butterfly garden
Hiking in Kauaranga Valley
Arts, shopping, dinning

Thames - 5 mins drive
Auckland - 1 hr 30 mins drive

THE HEIGHTS B&B

Grafton Rd

Parawai Rd

Bank St

25   To Auckland

From SH25 in Thames turn onto Bank Street, then right into Parawai Rd and finally left into Grafton Road. The Heights B&B is on the right, across from where Millington Place joins Grafton Road. Look for the sign

As I drove along the lush, flat Hauraki Plains I wondered how anything could be called The Heights. Up the short, sharp hill on the outskirts of Thames we found our destination. Turn around, look back and the stunning view sprawls in front of you right out to the Firth of Thames and beyond. I am welcomed inside by Phil and Vicky who are perfects hosts, we sit and chat over drinks with the most divine home baked biscuits and cheese. The Heights has two guest rooms, the Te Moana suite with superking bed has it own deck looking out over the plains and the glorious sunset. The Te Koru room complete with a very romantic fireplace makes the most of the garden. A very pleasant place to sit and enjoy a few hours with a book. If you are lucky you may be joined by one of the very exotic cats, although they like to spend time exploring. Phil originally from England and Vicki an American have both done much traveling and love entertaining people. This is evident by their attention to detail to ensure the guests every need is catered for. Thames is just a short one and a half hours from Auckland and is the perfect place to stop for a day or so before exploring the Coromandel Peninsula, Our hosts were only to happy to help us plan and make the most of our time. We quickly made a decision to rest up here on our return.

Accommodation available (NZ$)	🧍	🧍🧍	+🧍	🛏	🛁	Family cat on site
2 Rooms	$185-210	$195-225		K	EN	

Breakfast: Special cooked
Evening meal: $50-60pp
Guest rooms:
Ambience:
Setting/location:

LOW   HIGH

Property features
Separate guest lounge
Historic places category 2
Historic home/antique furnishings
Local features
Historical significance
Coromandel stamper battery
Driving Creek railway and pottery
Art & craft galleries
Cafes and restaurants

Karamana (1872) Homestead

Judie and Ian Franklyn
84 Whangapoua Rd, Coromandel
Tel: 07 8667138   Mob: 0211468430
Fax: 07 8667138
reservations@karamanahomestead.com
www.lodgings.co.nz – keyword: karamana

Coromandel - 10 mins walk
Whitianga - 40 mins drive

On the coast road from Thames,
200 metres south of Coromandel
township, turn right into
Whangapoua Rd. Karamana is
approx. 1km on the right on a
sharp right-hand bend.

What a gem! This 1872 kauri villa has been passionately restored, lovingly furnished with antiques and is now a four star boutique, intimate guesthouse. Karamana was rescued from obscurity and transformed into bed and breakfast accommodation 15 years ago and is a category 2 Historic Places listing. Present owners Judie and Ian continue the Victorian colonial theme. On the hot summer day I visited I enjoyed a glass of wine in the shade of the gazebo on the front lawn. Inside, the old parlour is now the dining room, a sun filled room overlooking the garden and a fitting venue for your silver service breakfast. I stayed in both double rooms but particularly fell in love with the king size four poster, Scottish antique bed in the Victorian room. The Cadman Room is at the front of the house and overlooks the garden. Judie and Ian's hospitality is definitely not intrusive and I was left to my own devices whenever I wanted. The Stables Cottage, across the courtyard is great if you want absolute privacy and it can be semi self catering. Karamana is an easy walk to Coromandel Township which has several good restaurants. In keeping with the historical theme we recommend the one hour tour of the Coromandel Gold Stamper Battery.

Breakfast: Special continental

Guest rooms:
Ambience:
Setting/location:

LOW   HIGH

Accommodation available (NZ$)	👤	👤👤	+👤	🛏	🛁
1 Room	$150	$175-225		K	EN
1 Room	$150	$175-225		Q	EN
1 Cottage		$175-225	$50	Q + 2S	EN

Gull Cottage

Geoff & Sharon Dalzell
6 Dawn Avenue, Hahei Beach
Tel: 07 8663311   Mob: 0272767644
Fax: 07 8686435
geoff@gullcottage-hahei.co.nz
www.lodgings.co.nz – keyword: gullcottage

Property features
Central location
Purpose built serviced apartment
Private decking/gas BBQ
Sports equipment available
Local features
Hot Water Beach - 10 mins drive
Cathedral Cove - 40 mins walk
Hahei Beach - 2 mins walk
Shops/restaruants - 2 mins walk
Fishing charters

Whitianga - 30 mins drive
Thames - 70 mins drive

Once you arrive in Hahei, you'll find Dawn Avenue on the right hand side of Hahei Beach Road (main road), almost immediately after the Hahei General Store (on your left). Gull Cottage is signposted at the beginning of Dawn Ave.

Pulling up at the gates, Geoff and Sharon are there to greet us, but they are not the only ones. There is Toby, a very lovable Jack Russell who quickly takes my place in the passenger seat and directs the driver to the car park outside our own apartment aptly named Gull Cottage. Within a few minutes we had settled into this two storied haven - dining area, bathroom and lounge downstairs and two bedrooms upstairs. The décor is very tasteful featuring items of furniture fashioned from recycled kauri timber recovered from historical buildings. The walls are adorned with local art. Geoff and Sharon had kindly left a superb antipasto plate, with homemade preserves, fruits, and cheeses. A bottle of wine was also chilling. We adjourned to the deck. There is a choice of two, one up and one down. A great way to relax after a long journey. Gull Cottage is only minutes from the world renowned Cathedral Cove and a short drive to Hot Water Beach where hot springs bubble up in the tidal zone. Our hosts have thought of everything including a spade so you can dig your own bath. It is just a short walk around the corner to restaurants or take the ferry to Whitianga, a ten minute drive away. I just have to mention the fabulous breakfast the next morning with freshly baked hot bread. We were sorry to leave here. Shame Toby was not back in the car as we left.

Accommodation available (NZ$)	👤	👥	+👤	🛏	🛁	Family pets on site Guest pets by arrangement
1 S/C cottage	$225	$225	$25	Q + 2S	PR	Breakfast: Continental

Guest rooms:
Ambience:
Setting/location:

LOW   HIGH

COROMANDEL PENINSULA - Waihi - Katikati - Tauranga - Whakatane - Opotiki - Gisborne - Hawkes Bay - Woodville - Martinborough

Property features
Swimming pool/spa pool
Private patios for each guest room
Panoramic views of Tairua estuary,
Pauanui/ Pacific Ocean/Slipper Island
All guest rooms are ensuite
Local features
Tairua Village - 15 min walk
White sandy beaches - 5 mins walk
Cathedral Cove - 1/2 hour drive
Hotwater Beach - 1/2 hour drive

Colleith Lodge
Maureen and Colin Gilroy
8 Rewa Rewa Valley Road, Tairua,
Coromandel Peninsula
Tel: 07 8647970   Mob: 021996100
Fax: 07 8647972
welcome@colleithlodge.co.nz
www.lodgings.co.nz – keyword: colleithlodge

    15

Thames - 35 mins drive
Auckland - 2 hour drive

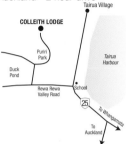

From Whangamata, take SH 25 north to Tairua. Just after the 50km sign, turn left into Rewa Rewa Valley Road. Turn right over cause-way and right into Puriri Park. Travel up hill to Colleith Lodge at top on left.

Set on a hill surrounded by one-and-a half acres of native bush, Colleith Lodge in the pretty seaside town of Tairua on the Coromandel Peninsula, has quality furnishings, comfortable spaces and tranquil surroundings. Sweeping panoramic views welcomed me from every room; Tairua Harbour, Pauanui, Slipper Island and the stretching Pacific Ocean. The green of New Zealand native bush and the green and blues of the Pacific Ocean were complimented by the honey-coloured hues of the kiln-dried, Hinuera natural stone that the lodge is built of. My queen-size bedroom with ensuite opened to a private patio, one of three bedrooms overlooking the swimming and spa pools and beyond to the ocean. In the early evening I sipped the New Zealand wine I'd chosen from the underground cellar and relaxed in one of the spacious living areas, before sitting down to a pre-arranged, three-course meal with Maureen and Colin. The following morning's breakfast included fresh tropical fruits grown on the property and an option of cooked dishes. For a day trip, Cathedral Cove and Hotwater Beach are both only a short 25-minute drive away. Colin is happy to arrange fishing trips for enthusiasts or guests are welcome to wander across the water in the two kayaks provided.

Family dog on site	Accommodation available (NZ$)				
Breakfast: Special cooked Evening meal: $70	3 Rooms	$395-450	$450-495	2Q+1SK	3 EN

Guest rooms:
Ambience:
Setting/location:

LOW   HIGH

Phone in hall/flat screen TV, DVD in all rooms/evening meals by prior arrangement/wine from cellar available at extra cost.

Harbour View Lodge

Eve and Alan Roper
179 Main Road, Tairua, Coromandel
Tel: 07 8647040
Fax: 07 8647042
info@harbourviewlodge.co.nz
www.lodgings.co.nz – keyword: harbourview

Property features
Swimming pool
Patio area & decks
Tairua harbour & Paku views
Broadband Internet (complimentary)
Laundry Service (complimentary)
Local features
Beach - 10 mins drive
Restaurants - 5 mins walk
Hot Water Beach - 20 mins drive
Cathedral Cove - 20 mins drive
Golf course - 5 mins drive

Tairua - 5 mins walk
Thames - 40 mins drive

From SH1 south of Auckland drive east on SH25 to Kopu. Continue on SH25A over the hills to Hikuai, continue 9km to Tairua. Harbour View Lodge is on your left on the main road approx 1 km from Tairua Village

The Coromandel Peninsula is a superb location to share in the great kiwi tradition - the summer holiday at the beach. Harbour View is situated right in the very heart of Tairua with its cafés, galleries and wonderful holiday atmosphere. This purpose built bed and breakfast with views from the upstairs dining room over the inlet towards the mountains has three spacious ensuite bedrooms and a guest lounge which adjourns a patio with an inviting swimming pool. The rooms are beautifully decorated with fine linens and personal touches to ensure that our holiday was relaxing and memorable. There is however plenty to do, being so conveniently close to all amenities, the inlet ferry to Pauanui golf courses, fishing and just 20 minutes from Hotwater Beach and Cathedral Cove. Our hosts Eve and Alan were only too happy to point us in the right direction with advice on what to do and how to make the most of our time. It was also just so easy to just kick back and do nothing at all with a wine in hand and our feet dangling in to pool telling stories. That's what a kiwi summer is all about.

Accommodation available (NZ$)	👤	👤👤	+👤	🛏	🛁	Family dog on site
2 Rooms	$190	$220	$30	Q	EN	Breakfast: Special cooked
1 Room	$190	$220	$30	SK or 2S	EN	

Phone, Sky TV, DVDs and videos available in guest lounge.

Guest rooms:
Ambience:
Setting/location:

LOW   HIGH

Property features
Rural setting surrounded by bush
Expansive coastal views
Spa pool
Wireless broadband
Peaceful and relaxing
Local features
Walkways/golf course/fishing
Gold mines/vintage trains
Cathedral Cove & Hotwater beach
Farm visits/white sandy beach
Hot natural mineral pools

Poets Corner Lodge

John and Marg Ritchie
28 Poets Corner Road, Waihi
Tel: 07 8633091   Mob: 021435012
Fax: 07 8633092
info@poetscornerlodge.co.nz
www.lodgings.co.nz – keyword: poetscorner

Ⓟ 🚶 ✉ ♿

Waihi - 7 mins drive
Tauranga - 45 mins drive

From Waihi follow the signs to
Whangamata (SH25), take the road
to Golden Valley (Barry Road) on the
right. After 3 km turn right into Trig
Road continue for 1km, turn left into
Heard Road, continue for 2km then
turn left into Poets Corner Road.

   Heading out of the historic gold mining town of Waihi, through picturesque farmland, then sharply uphill you could be forgiven for asking the question where are we heading. Turn the last corner and up the lane to Poets Corner Lodge and you will find yourself on a ridge at the top of the world – The surprises don't stop. Step up to the enormous wooden gates and enter a haven of good taste, design and tranquility – the four tastefully decorated units featuring local artists are centered around an enclosed courtyard. Cleverly designed to equally accommodate a group of four couples traveling together or provide peace and relaxation for a couple. It is only natural however to gravitate to the guest lounge and deck to take in the spectacular views which span 180° from Mt Manganui in the south to Slipper Island to the North, the next stop Chile! A gourmet breakfast is also served in this room. Marg and John and their best friend Bella, an adorable retriever live next door and are only to happy to help with information on the surrounding area. Waihi is the gateway to both the Coromandel and the Bay of Plenty and there is no shortage of interesting activities, a helicopter visit to White Island and 1 ½ hours drive away from Hotwater Beach & Cathedral Cove. Poets Corner, on the road to the sky is a true delight.

Accommodation available (NZ$)	🧍	🧍🧍	+🧍	🛏	🛁
4 Rooms	$350	$350		SK/T	EN

Breakfast: Cooked
Evening meal: $65pp
Guest rooms:
Ambience:
Setting/location:

LOW   HIGH

Laundry, packed lunch, transport on request.

Waihi Beach Lodge

Greg Whyte Ali Lawn
170 Seaforth Road, Waihi Beach
Tel: 07 8635818   Mob: 021657888
Fax: 07 8635815
waihi.beach.lodge@xtra.co.nz
www.lodgings.co.nz – keyword: waihibeach

(P) ✉ 📺   MasterCard VISA eftpos ♿

Property features
Sea and rural views
Relaxing/decks/outdoor areas
2 minute stroll to beach
Wireless internet connection
Private guest entrances
TV and DVD's in all rooms
Local features
Handy to local café's
Karangahape Gorge walkways
Handy to golf courses
Mayor Island sightseeing/fishing

Tauranga - 40 mins drive
Auckland - 2 hours drive

2 hours from Auckland International
Airport. The Waihi Beach turn-off is
off State Highway 2 between Waihi
and Katikati. Wilson Road becomes
Seaforth Road which runs the length
of Waihi Beach.

Waihi Beach Lodge is an easy two-hour, scenic drive south of Auckland. Ali and Greg have created this new bed and breakfast 'beach getaway', which is located on the main road running parallel to the beach. It is a perfect place to stay for anyone wishing to explore the eastern coastline of the North Island, or for those who simply want to escape the city. The Beach Suite, on the ground floor at the rear of the house, is a beautifully decorated, studio-style unit. It has a queen-size bed, a pull-out couch, a dining table, television and DVD. There's also a small kitchenette, laundry and ensuite bathroom. There are also three guestrooms with ensuites, king-size beds, DVDs, televisions, and tea/coffee making facilities. Three rooms have doors leading out to their very own private sun drenched terraced areas, great for reading a book or just relaxing with a glass of wine enjoying the views of Mayor Island, the Pacific Ocean and listening to the sound of the waves breaking on the shore. Breakfast is served upstairs in the dining room or al fresco on one of the patios. After a weekend at Waihi Beach Lodge, the beach walks, fishing, exploring the eastern coastline, and great breakfasts, I left feeling relaxed and rejuvenated.

Accommodation available (NZ$)	🧍	🧍🧍	+🧍	🛏	🛁	
3 Rooms	$265	$265		K	EN	Breakfast: Special cooked
1 S/C unit	$265	$265	$50	Q	PR	Evening meal: $50pp

Guest rooms:
Ambience:
Setting/location:

LOW   HIGH

Property features
- Quiet stress free privacy in rural setting
- Renowned gardens
- Private deck overlooking gully/creek
- SKY TV/DVD/Mp3/stereo/laundry
- Perfect for honeymoons

Local features
- Mural Town - 5 mins drive
- Bush walks/beach/river/harbour
- 2 excellent golf courses
- Restaurants/cafés/wineries nearby

Katikati - 5 mins drive
Tauranga - 35 mins drive

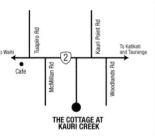

On State Highway Two, five minutes north of Katikati, fifteen minutes south of Waihi, between Kauri Point Road and McMillan Road.

The Cottage at Kauri Creek

Norm and Joanne Knight
469 State Highway 2, RD 1, Katikati
Tel: 07 5491104   Mob: 0272812627
Fax: 07 5491102
info@kauricreekcottage.co.nz
www.lodgings.co.nz – keyword: kauricreek

The Cottage at Kauri Creek is less than two hours from central Auckland and is close to all attractions in the Bay of Plenty. Leaving the madness of the highway, we were enchanted by the pheasants, rabbits and pukekos that scurried away as we drove up the long oak tree-lined driveway towards The Cottage - we immediately felt the peace and tranquillity. Joanne and Norm warmly welcomed us, and after ensuring all our needs were met, left us to settle into our home away from home. Fine linen, and modern conveniences ensured we felt utterly relaxed. Intrigued by the surrounding beauty, we wandered into our private garden and found a sundeck perched on the hillside overlooking a lush green gully where animals grazed in the late afternoon sun - we sat and listened to the sound of the waterfall below us in the creek. For 26 years the property has been a rose and citrus nursery and the large rambling garden reflects this, with old fashioned roses in abundance. The hosts are semi-retired yet their enthusiasm for plants and gardening remains strong and they are happy to share this with guests who have similar interests. We enjoyed this pretty country-styled cottage, casually intimate with the very best of fresh breakfast provisions supplied each morning.

Accommodation available (NZ$)			+		
1 S/C cottage	$180-250	$180-250	$25	Q + sofa bed	EN

Breakfast: Provisions provided

Guest rooms:
Ambience:
Setting/location:

LOW   HIGH

Boscabel Lodge

Rosemary and Peter Luxton
98D Boscabel Drive, Ohauiti, Tauranga
Tel: 07 5446647   Mob: 021744441
Fax: 07 5446647
boscabellodge@yahoo.com
www.lodgings.co.nz – keyword: boscabel

(P) 林 ☒ ☐ (C)

Property features
Solar heated swimming pool & spa
New architectually designed lodge
Honeymoon suite
Bush walk nearby
Landscaped grounds
Local features
Swim with dolphins
Watersports/outdoor activities
Mt. Maunganui/fishing/golfing
Vineyards/wineries
Beaches/cafes

Tauranga - 5 mins drive
Rotorua - 1 hour drive

From SH 29 or SH 2 go towards Welcome Bay. Turn east into Welcome Bay Rd. Take the first right into Ohauiti Rd. Travel 3km and turn into Boscabel Dr. The lodge is towards the end down a shared drive.

The lodge is a large, modern mansion on a rise overlooking a sweep of rural and suburban land and the distant outline of the Kaimanawa Ranges, Mt. Maunganui and Mayor Island. Not long ago it was an avocado orchard. Rosemary and Peter and their two children are New Zealanders who arrived back in the country and decided to put down roots in this sunny corner of the North Island. The house has many notable features. The colours and patterns of the Feng Shui tiling that covers the floors, patios and outdoor areas is integrated with the colourful drapes and furnishings. There are extensive spaces open to the sun and view and the ambience is cheerful and inviting. I stayed in one of the two family apartments, which are exceptionally roomy, with one double bedroom, one twin, a modern bathroom, fully furnished lounge and a kitchen with everything supplied. They are suitable for long-term stays. There is also a smaller suite for over-nighters. My apartment opened to a solar heated swimming pool, the spa pool and the extensive landscaped garden dotted with avocado trees. Special continental breakfasts are served to the apartments by arrangement. Staying here was a very pleasant experience.

Accommodation available (NZ$)	👤	👥	+👤	🛏	🛁	
1 Suite	$125	$150-160		Q	EN	Breakfast: Special continental
1 S/C unit	$145	$160-185		K+2S	PR	
1 S/C unit	$145	$160-185		Q+2S	PR	Guest rooms:

Family dog on site

Breakfast: Special continental

Guest rooms:
Ambience:
Setting/location:

LOW   HIGH

Breakfast included in suite. Breakfast not included in S/C units, $10pp.

Property features
Swimming pool
Finish dry sauna
Large garden
Organic cattle farm
Beach - 1 min walk
Local features
Active marine volcano, White Island
Swimming with dolphins
Te Urewera National Park
Game fishing/trout fishing
Rotorua Lakes/watersports

Whakatane - 25 mins drive
Te Puke - 25 mins drive

From Te Puke travel east on the Pacific Coast Hwy (SH2), continue for 33.6km, look for signpost with blue B&B traffice signs.

Pohutukawa Beach B&B and Cottage

Jorg and Charlotte Prinz
693 State Highway 2, Pikowai
Tel: 07 3222182
Fax: 07 3222186
bnb@prinztours.co.nz
www.lodgings.co.nz – keyword: pohutukawa

(P) 👫 📺   MasterCard VISA

I drove from the seaside highway up a short steep driveway to be met at the gate by a jubilant dog called Vivaldi. Smoke was drifting from the chimney of this renovated and redecorated farmhouse which has two comfortable and pleasantly decorated ensuite bedrooms for guests, a roomy lounge and dining area with large windows that face the sea. I immediately relaxed into the place, feeling as if I had come home. On the 34-acre hill farm, a small herd of organic cattle grazes and on the flat land, there is an orchard of citrus and feijoa trees and an organic vegetable garden. Much of my dinner that night was home grown. To one side of the house is an enclosed sunny courtyard with a swimming pool and sauna, and on the other side of that a well-appointed cottage which sleeps four. From the house and its extensive front garden there is a close view of sand dunes and sea through the spreading branches of a large pohutukawa tree. Sitting at breakfast guests can be lucky enough to see a pod of whales or dolphin slide by. Even orcas sometimes come close into shore. This place is a destination not just a place to overnight. It is better to stay more than one day if you can and consider joining Jorg's guided tour of the Bay of Plenty.

Family pets on site

	Accommodation available (NZ$)	👤	👤👤	+👤	🛏	🛁
Breakfast: Special continental	1 Room	$100	$120		K or 2S	EN
Evening meal: $35pp	1 Room	$100	$120		Q	EN
Guest rooms:	1 S/C house		$160-180	$30-40	Q+D	PR
Ambience:						
Setting/location:						

LOW   HIGH

85

Capeview Cottage

Brian and Kathleen Young
167 Tablelands Road, Opotiki, Bay of Plenty
Tel: 07 3157877
Fax: 07 3158055   Free: 0800227384
kyoung@capeview.co.nz
www.lodgings.co.nz – keyword: capeview

Brian and Kathleen Young
167 Tablelands Road, Opotiki, Bay of Plenty
Tel: 07 3157877
Fax: 07 3158055   Free: 0800227384
kyoung@capeview.co.nz

(P) 🚶 📺 ☎

Property features
Spectacular views
Peace and tranquility
Outdoor hot-tub/satellite TV
DVD/home theatre stereo system
Fully S/C with kitchen & laundry
Local features
Golf course - 10 mins
Jet boating - 40 mins
Safe swimming beaches - 3 mins
Sea & river fishing/bush walks
White Island - volcano

Whakatane - 45 mins drive
Rotorua - 1hr 45 mins drive

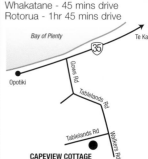

CAPEVIEW COTTAGE

Follow the Capeview signs from SH
35 (Opotiki to Te Kaha). The cottage
is 4km from Opotiki.

Perched high on rolling hills with wide views of the East Cape mountains and the distant ocean, this self-contained retreat is best described as luxurious. The location is a great stopover en-route to Gisborne or East Cape. There comes a time in any long journey when it is right to take time out, cook your own food, catch up on the washing and take it easy for a day or two. What better way to do that than in this modern, purpose-built, secluded, fully equipped cottage? Inside I found a full kitchen (including a dishwasher), laundry facilities, bathroom (with bath) and a separate lounge/dining area. Upstairs there are two, well-appointed, large bedrooms each with leather seating. Apart from views, the most memorable thing about the cottage is the comfort. Details, such as a coffee plunger, the sweet temptations, DVD player, Sky television and the well-appointed furnishings left me wanting for nothing. The cottage is only a short walk to the main home and so the seclusion is without isolation. One great way to spend an evening at Capeview Cottage is to admire the view and the star-filled night sky from the steaming hot-tub. You are guaranteed to feel refreshed, strong and ready for the road.

Accommodation available (NZ$)	🧍	🧍🧍	+🧍	🛏	🛁
1 S/C cottage	$145	$145	$30	2SK or 4S	PR

Meals available on request. First night $145, additional nights $130.

Family pets on site
Guest pets by arrangement

Breakfast: Extra $15pp
Evening meal: $35pp
Guest rooms:
Ambience:
Setting/location:

LOW   HIGH

Property features
Breathtaking views
Overlooks vinegards & olive grove
BBQ & full kitchen
Estate Chardonnay & olive oil
Wireless internet available

Local features
Eastwoodhill arboretum
Beaches/swimming/surfing
Hot pools/fishing/diving
Golf courses/driving range
Adventure walks/wineries

Gisborne - 15 mins drive
Wairoa - 60 mins drive

From Gisborne city centre, travel south
west on Grey Street, at roundabout take
Awapuni Rd exit. After 6.8km turn left
onto Wharerata Rd SH2, at roundabout
turn into Wharekopae Rd, turn right into
Patutahi Rd, turn left onto Atkins St, right
onto Lavenham Rd, left onto Lake Rd,
left onto Repongaere Rd.

Repongaere Estate

Bevan & Julie Turnpenny
30 Repongaere Road, Patuhahui, Gisborne
Tel: 06 8627515   Mob: 021375387
Fax: 06 8627687
stay@repongaere.co.nz
www.lodgings.co.nz – keyword: repongaere

Gisborne, the first in the world to see the light of day. There is something special about waking up to a new dawn. Step out on to the patio and look out over a sea of grape vines and olive trees and you could be forgiven for thinking it was the only place in the world to be. Repongaere boosts architecturally designed villas luxuriously furnished with every possible convenience ensuring that your holiday is nothing short of amazing. Two large bedrooms with a large central area for entertaining ensured we had all the space we could wish for. The property managed by Bevan and Julie Turnpenny are on hand to ensure that we wanted for nothing. Gisborne has a world wide reputation for its vineyards and what better way to integrate into the local culture than to take a tour of the vineyards sampling the Chardonnay that this region is known for. If and when the wines don't appeal then there is an array of water sports, yachting, wind surfing and of course the renowned surfing. Lake Waikaremoana is only 2 hours away if you wish to try your hand at trout fishing. After all that activity it seems only natural to relax in the hands of Julie who is a qualified masseuse. Stay a few days, enjoy one of the most beautiful climates in New Zealand and relish the fact you will be one of the first to start another exciting day.

Guest pets by arrangement

Breakfast: Continental
Evening meal: Available

Accommodation available (NZ$)	🧍	🧍🧍	+🧍	🛏	🛁
1 S/C villa	$220-265	$220-265	$30	1Q+2S	EN
1 S/C villa	$220-265	$220-265	$30	1Q+K/2S	EN
1 S/C villa	$220-265	$220-265	$30	1K+K/2S	EN
4 S/C units	$190-235	$220-265			EN

S/C units available from May 2008. Evening meals are available by prior arrangement.

Mollie's Cottage

Shirley De Luca
21 Sealy Road, Napier
Tel: 06 8358573   Mob: 0210477200
Fax: 06 8358573
delucamolliescottage@xtra.co.nz
www.lodgings.co.nz – keyword: molliescottage

Property features
Guest suite has private lounge
Close proximity to town
Two guests at a time
Quiet and peaceful
Laundry facilities/fridge
Local features
Art Deco Napier
Vineyards/wineries
Beaches
Gannet colony
Historical walks/gardens

Napier - 5 mins walk
Hastings - 25 mins drive

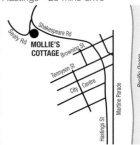

From Marine Parade, head into Hastings Street and continue north as the road changes it's name to Shakespeare Road. The entrance is at no. 64. Thereafter garage parking is available at 21 Sealy Road.

What a fantastic place to stay. When I am travelling, I always seem to have far too much luggage. The guest suite at Mollie's Cottage is large with a separate living area so that I could store all my luggage and have a bedroom that didn't look like a tornado had hit it as soon as I had opened one of my bags. The living room is complete with small dining table, lounge furniture, television, fridge with tea and coffee making facilities and elevated view - very comfortable for a longer stay. My host, Shirley, describes the accommodation as quintessential - the décor is romantic, plush and luxurious. This is certainly honeymoon territory. Breakfast can be served either in the dining room in the house or in your private living area where you won't be disturbed. A walk down to Shakespeare Road means that you can be in the heart of Napier's city centre within minutes and enjoy the many cafes, restaurants, historical walks, gardens, Aquarium or just enjoy the Art Deco that Napier has to offer. There is a lock-up garage available to guests on the street adjacent the house.

Accommodation available (NZ$)						
1 Suite	$130-150	$150-180		SK/T	EN	Breakfast: Special cooked/continental

Guest rooms:
Ambience:
Setting/location:

LOW   HIGH

Property features
Professional Chef
Large gardens
Petanque court
Rural setting
Views of the hills and vineyards
Local features
Napiers Art Deco
Cape Kidnappers golf course
Vineyards and wineries
Trout fishing/red & sika deer hunting
Chocolate factory

Napier - 15 mins drive
Hastings - 15 mins drive

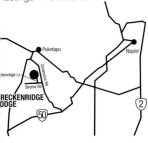

Breckenridge Lodge is just a short 15min drive from Napier. Please refer to the website for detailed driving instructions or contact the host Malcolm.

Breckenridge Lodge

Malcolm Redmond
1 Breckenridge Lane, RD 3, Napier
Tel: 06 8449411   Mob: 0276649800
Fax: 06 8449410
indulge@breckenridgelodge.co.nz
www.lodgings.co.nz – keyword: breckenridge

A purpose built lodge, set into well tended gardens above a sea of vines. Breckenridge has a lot to offer. It's deep in the Hawkes Bay wine country yet only a short drive from Napier's Art Deco attractions. No immediate neighbours and a no exit road promises peace and quite. But not too quiet. Malcolm's a master chef. It's a Breckenridge specialty to design the evening meal to guest fancy. Give him an idea of favourite food, he will not only produce a designed-for-you 5 course meal of local produce, but match it with local wines. Want to spend the day on a wine trail? What about Art Deco interest, or the areas many tourist attractions? Choices, choices. Here's a unique alternative, spend the afternoon in Malcolm's kitchen learning to prepare your own designer dinner! He does offer cooking courses. Something a little more active after all this indulgence? There's golf close by, or Malcolm's happy to arrange local fishing or hunting excursions. Stay at Breckenridge for a point of difference, for its peaceful position, delightful surroundings and Malcolm's food magic....

	Accommodation available (NZ$)	🧍	🧍🧍	+🧍	🛏	🛁
Family cat on site Guest pets by arrangement						
Breakfast: Special cooked	5 rooms	$450	$500		K or 2S	EN

Guest rooms:
Ambience:
Setting/location:

LOW   HIGH

Dinner, bed and breakfast $575 single - $750 double.

Muritai

Denis and Margie Hardy
68 Duart Road, Havelock North
Tel: 06 8777588   Mob: 0274443800
Fax: 06 8760275
endsleigh.cottages@xtra.co.nz
www.lodgings.co.nz - keyword: muritai

Property features
Extensive gardens
Antique furniture
Significant contemporary NZ Art
Full lifestyle sound system
Chip and putting green
Croquet sets/petanque court

Local features
The amenities of Havelock North and surrounding districts
Vineyards/wineries - 5 mins
Golf courses/beaches - 5 mins

Havelock North - 3 mins drive
Hastings - 8 mins drive

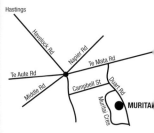

From roundabout in Havelock North village, take the Te Mata Road to the north-east. Turn right into Duart Road. Muritai is on the right.

Up a winding driveway through weeping trees and rhododendron bushes is this historic, low-slung, weatherboard homestead which was one of several major houses established in the area in the 1890's. With its occupants this gracious dwelling, now restored and modernised, played an important part in the area's early history. A photograph taken in 1899 shows it surrounded by emptiness. Today it is in the middle of Havelock North's dress circle of homes. There are five double bedrooms, one twin single and a single bedroom and five full bathrooms and a separate bathroom for non resident guests - the house sleeps 13 comfortably. All the larger rooms have their own entrance from the large verandahs that surround the house. The furnishings (much of it antique) and the décor are lavish and in keeping with the era the house was built in, but there are also modern paintings, central heating, hair driers, toiletries, Sky television and music systems to all the main rooms. Although the modern kitchen is set up for self-catering, outside caterers can be arranged to prepare dinner for serving in the magnificent formal dining room or large outdoor patio, while guests relax in the spacious lounge. This is a wonderful place for a weekend house party.

Accommodation available (NZ$)					
1 S/C house		$1000			

Single party bookings $1000 per night.

Breakfast: Provisions provided
Evening meal: $50pp
Guest rooms:
Ambience:
Setting/location:

LOW   HIGH

Property features
Petanque lawns
Croquet lawn/tennis court
Video and Sky TV
CD system
Mountain bikes
Antique cottage furniture
Cottage gardens

Local features
Trout fishing - guides available
Vineyards/wineries - 5 mins
Golf courses - 5 mins

Havelock North - 5 mins drive
Hastings - 10 mins drive

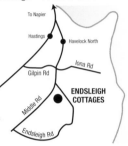

From Havelock North village, turn into Middle Road. Travel for 2km, and turn left into Endsleigh Rd. Endsleigh Cottages is the second drive on the right.

Endsleigh Cottages

Margie and Denis Hardy
Endsleigh Rd and Middle Rd, Havelock North
Tel: 06 8777588   Mob: 0274443800
Fax: 06 8760275
endsleigh.cottages@xtra.co.nz
www.lodgings.co.nz – keyword: endsleigh

Margie and Denis provide self-contained, self-catering accommodation in three charming cottages situated in the Havelock North hills among gardens and trees on a semi-rural property, not far from the centre of the town. Each cottage reflects the style of earlier days but has all the comfort and convenience of today. Two cottages were brought to the site and restored using traditional methods and the third was built with recycled timber. The smaller cottage dates from the early 1900's; the larger cottages are fully equipped houses with kitchen, laundries, bathrooms, separate bedrooms and attractive sitting rooms with comfortable sofas and open fires. The bedrooms are separate and one has an additional ensuite double bedroom. The main rooms in these cottages open onto wrap-around verandahs with rural views and are sunny and peaceful. In summer they are popular for barbecues and lunches or evening drinks. I stayed in the small cottage, which is big on charm and has a large bedroom and bathroom. It is great for a night or two and the larger cottages are more suitable for longer stay. Mountain bikes are provided if guests want to cycle around the village and hills and they are welcome to use the lawn tennis court.

Family cat on site
Guest pets by arrangement

Breakfast: Provisions provided
Evening meal: $50pp
Guest rooms:
Ambience:
Setting/location:

LOW   HIGH

Accommodation available (NZ$)	👤	👤👤	+👤	🛏	🛁
1 Cottage	$100	$100		Q	PR
1 S/C cottage		$200	$50	Q	PR
2 bed Cottage		$250	$50	Q+D	PR+EN

Peach Gully Cottage

Craig and Kristal Foss
2006 Waimarama Rd, Waimarama Beach,
Hawkes Bay
Tel: 06 8746009   Mob: 021566701
cottage@peachgully.co.nz
www.lodgings.co.nz – keyword: peachgully

Property features
Rural setting/historic homestead
View over Pacific Ocean
Bush/farm/waterfall walk
Heated pool in season
Tennis/petanque courts
BBQ/brazier/log fire
Selection of wine for purchase
Local features
Swimming/surf beach - 5 min
Golf course - 15 min
Wineries/restaurants - 15 min
Havelock North - 20 mins drive
Napier - 40 mins drive

From Havelock Nth, follow signs to
Waimarama. After approx 20km, you
reach the crest of a hill and below
you is Waimarama beach. From the
vantage point, Peach Gully is 500m
on the right.

Every once in a while I found myself at a place that I never wanted to leave. Peach Gully Cottage is one of them. Tucked away on a large private section is a cute, fairytale, one-bedroom cottage that is charming, luxurious and full of character. Built in 1914, it has been restored and re-decorated with contemporary furniture and modern comforts. The bathroom of Peach Gully Cottage, with its old claw-foot bath, is delightful and the kitchen has all mod cons, including a microwave and dishwasher. The great stretch of Waimarama Beach is only a short drive away and the position of the cottage is ideal, not only for a summer stay, but as a romantic winter retreat. Hosts, Craig and Kristal, provide the fresh ingredients for breakfast but guests provide any other meals for themselves. I stocked up while I was in the township of Havelock North, which is about a twenty-minute drive away. The large garden surrounding the cottage is shared with the host's home and set into it are a tennis court and a swimming pool. I enjoyed a quick dip and then went for a short, fresh walk across the farm.

Accommodation available (NZ$)						Family dog on site
1 S/C cottage		$320		Q	PR	Breakfast: Provisions provided

Guest rooms:
Ambience:
Setting/location:

Minimum 2 nights stay. Seasonal rates apply.

Property features
Inground pool with entertaining area
Summer house
Lawn croquet/petanque/library
Formal Victorian Gothic dining room
Cocktail/reception areas
Local features
Hertitage trails/art galleries
Indoor pool complex with modern gym
Golf Courses/restaurants 5 mins

Woburn Homestead
Heatha Edwards and Philip Allerby
216 Hatuma Road, RD 1, Waipukurau
Tel: 06 8589668   Mob: 0274529112
heatha@woburnhomestead.co.nz
www.lodgings.co.nz – keyword: woburn

Waipukurau - 5 mins drive
Havelock North - 25 mins drive

From South Take SH 2 from
Woodville, Hatuma Rd is 2km south of
Waipukurau. Woburn Homestead is two
2km on the right. From north SH2 2km
past Waipukurau.

This 1893 built home was the Grand Manor of a 13,000 acre estate. New Zealand's early history saw land grants to settlers determined and in 1901 Woburn Estate was divided up with the Crown reclaiming and reallocating to many individual farms. Today the homestead stands on 4 acres of fertile river plain, surrounded by a sea of traditional New Zealand sheep and cattle agriculture. Owners Heatha and Philip are passionate about the area's history. "Houses like this are special. They will never be built again. We need to look after them," declares Heatha. And that's just what they are doing. But whilst every effort is being made to restore originality, the homestead is no museum piece. The rooms have all been beautifully presented with chandeliers, antique furniture, and fine furnishings and fireplaces. All the suites are in keeping with the era. This family is energetic, warm and welcoming and Woburn a grand place for that special occasion Whilst the area isn't 'tourist trail', it will be, as more and more folk discover the Ruahine Range tramping trails, beautiful white sand beaches and the excellent undiscovered trout fishing. Stay at Woburn for glimpses of early NZ agriculture, to get off the beaten path awhile, and for Heatha's wonderful kiwi cooking!

Family dog on site	Accommodation available (NZ$)	👤	👥	+👤	🛏	🛁
Breakfast: Special cooked	1 Room	$150	$250	$75	Q+KS	EN
Evening meal: $45pp	1 Room	$150	$250		2S	EN
Guest rooms:	1 Room	$300	$300		Q	EN
Ambience:						
Setting/location:		A luxuriously restored landmark Historic Place Trust Home.				

LOW   HIGH

Otawa Lodge

Del and Sue Trew
132 Otawhao Road, Kumeroa, RD 1, Woodville
Tel: 06 3764603   Mob: 0272301327
rest@otawalodge.co.nz
www.lodgings.co.nz – keyword: otawa

Property features
Historic homestead/mature garden
Guest sitting room & library
Native bush & hill walks
Central heating
Creative cuisine/selected wine list
Local features
Antique shops
Fishing/hunting/skydiving/tramping
Te Apiti/Tararua Wind Farm
Lavender farm visits/wind farm
Gottfried Lindauer Studio

Woodville - 15 mins drive
Dannevirke - 20 mins drive

4kms north of Woodville on SH 2 turn
right onto Hopelands Rd to Kumeroa.
Travel 6.1 km, cross river and turn left
into Kumeroa Rd. At junction with Tota
Rd, Kumeroa Rd becomes Otawhao F
Lodge on right just past Cemetery Rd.

A narrow road that snakes into the hills from the township of Kumeroa leads to this magnificent homestead in the Otawhao Valley. The large house is one of the finest examples of Art Noveau architecture in the country and captures all the style of the Edwardian era. Sue and Del have meticulously restored the old house to its original elegance. I really enjoyed the detail - the stained leaded glass windows, ceilings and walls of intricate plasterwork and timber panelling with Art Nouveau furnishings, tiling and door handles completing the decor. Guests have exclusive use of the north wing where the large comfortable sitting room with its own verandah overlooks the gardens and hills. Leading off this room is a sunny octagonal library. Accommodation is in two luxurious bedrooms with private bathrooms. The hosts live in the other wing of the house and dedicate their time to looking after their guests. The four-course dinners and the breakfasts are served formally in the dining area. Sue specialises in innovative fish dishes. By day visitors can enjoy the extensive garden with its mature trees, take a picnic to the old waterwheel or venture further afield to walk in the native bush, go fishing, or look for antique bargains in nearby Woodville.

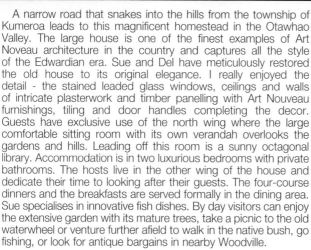

Accommodation available (NZ$)					
1 Room	$265-295	Q	PR	Breakfast: Special cooked
1 Room	$265-295	K or 2S	PR	Evening meal: $85pp
				Guest rooms:
				Ambience:
				Setting/location:

Broadband internet available in sitting room/library. Phone in hall.

LOW   HIG

Property features
Spa pool
Sky TV
Billiard room
Petanque
Local features
Golf course - 5 min drive
Vine tasting
Restaurants - 5 min walk
4WD quad bikes - 10 min drive
Cape Palliser seal colony - 45 min drive
Hot air ballooning - 15 min drive

The Old Manse

John and Sandra Hargrave
19 Grey Street, Martinborough
Tel: 06 3068599   Mob: 0274399229
Fax: 06 3068540   Free: 0800399229
john@oldmanse.co.nz
www.lodgings.co.nz – keyword: oldmanse

Martinborough - 5 mins walk

ake SH2 and 53 to
Martinborough. Once in town, take
the first right into Princess Street.
Turn right at end of St and left into
Roberts Street. The Old Manse
corner of Roberts and Grey Streets.

Set beside a vineyard in Martinborough, is a lovely, historic house, built in 1876, and now restored and enhanced to offer guests a home away from home. Hosts, Sandra and John, made me feel like part of their family and my stay was extremely comfortable. The property is well situated for couples who want to visit some of the many vineyards in the area. It is also an ideal venue for weddings and group gatherings. There are six guestrooms in the house. Each has a private ensuite. When I arrived, other guests were sharing a bottle of one of the region's fine wines and swapping stories about their day's exploring. I joined in and then took a short walk to the centre of town where several restaurants had menus offering a good range of choices for dinner. I slept peacefully at the Old Manse that night and awoke to the quiet countryside and the enticing aroma of a cooked breakfast being prepared by John. At breakfast Sandra was busy organising a tour of the vineyards for other guests. Sadly, I had to move on. It felt a bit like leaving home; The Old Manse is a place I will particularly remember and to return to.

Accommodation available (NZ$)	👤	👥	+👤	🛏	🛁
5 Rooms			$170-210	Q	EN
1 Room			$170-210	2S	EN

Breakfast: Cooked

Guest rooms:
Ambience:
Setting/location:

LOW   HIGH

95

MARTINBOROUGH

Coromandel Peninsula - Waihi - Katikati - Tauranga - Whakatane - Opotiki - Gisborne - Hawkes Bay - Woodville - MARTINBOROUGH

Parehua Country Estate
Martinborough

Mike and Lois Kunac
New York Street, Martinborough, 5741
Tel: 06 3068405
Fax: 06 3068409   Free: 08004727382 (4PAREHUA)
info@parehua.co.nz
www.lodgings.co.nz – keyword: parehua

Property features
5 acres park like grounds
Private willow-fringed lake
Panorama views of countryside
Outdoor swimming pool
Tennis court/bikes avail. for hire
Wedding location
Local features
Martinborough wine village
Greytown - 12 mins drive
Golf course - 5 mins drive
Boutique vineyards - 5 mins drive

Martinborough Wine Village -
10 mins walk
Wellington City - 1 hr 30 mins drive

From Wellington follow SH2
to Featherston, follow sign to
Martinborough. You enter Martinborough
on Kitchener street, turn left into Princess
Street, first left into New York Street,
Parehua is at the end.

Just one hour from Wellington in the heart of the world class wine growing area of Martinborough there is a real gem, a destination. Parehua Country Estate, set on five acres of park like grounds has a mix of suites, cottages and two bedroom villas. The furnishings are exquisite and every detail has been attended to. Artworks in toning hues adorn the walls. All the rooms are spacious with fireplaces and outdoor areas however it was the clever design of bedroom verses entertaining area that impressed. Bathrooms and kitchens have also been given the lavish treatment. Martinborough is well known for its wineries and what better way than peddle power on one of the bikes supplied to get acquainted with the vines. There are also farm tours, quad bikes, golf and so many other attractions. Our choice was however to stay right here and enjoy a game of tennis, a swim followed by a glass of local wine overlooking the lake and the vineyard. What a perfect place for that romantic wedding. No need to stress with planning here. All that is taken care of for you. There is no shortage of cafes nearby so dinner was an easy option. Breakfast was an occasion in The Pavilion, a great place to attack the next day's activities. Talk about wow factor, Parehua Country Estate has it all.

Accommodation available (NZ$)	🧍	🧍🧍	+🧍	🛏	🛁	
8 S/C suites	$350	$350	K or 2S	EN		Breakfast: Cooked
8 S/C suites	$320-350	$320-350	K or 2S	EN		
6 S/C suites	$320-350	$320-350	K	EN		Guest rooms:
4 S/C cottages	$450	$450	K	EN		Ambience:
2 S/C villas		$600 (4 people)	2K or 4S	EN		Setting/location:

LOW   HIG

Abel Tasman Ocean View Chalets

Robert and Konstanca Palzer
Marahau Beach, Motueka
Tel: 03 5278232
Fax: 03 5278211
info@accommodationAbelTasman.co.nz
www.lodgings.co.nz – keyword: oceanview

Property features
Individual timber chalets
Breakfast/packed lunch available
Activity booking on site
Sea views/BBQ available
Cots and high chairs available
Local features
Walk Abel Tasman Coastal Trek
Sea kayaking
Beach walks
Horse trekking
Café/restaurant - 10 mins walk

Motueka - 20 mins drive
Nelson - 1 hour drive

From Nelson follow signs to Abel Tasman National Park on SH 60. Approx 6km from Motueka, turn off Marahau Beach. Ocean View Chalet is on the left, nearly at the end of th road.

Located on a 50-acre, coastal farm, each of these elevated self-contained Lawson Cyprus timber chalets has a view out to Marahau Beach and, in the distance, Tasman Bay, Fisherman Island, the Marlborough Sounds and Durville Island. There are three different styles of accommodation; open-plan studio, one-bedroom and two-bedroom chalets. Established native gardens surround each chalet ensuring guests' privacy, and the chalets are positioned to maximise the views. Each chalet has the same facilities including private parking, a fully equipped kitchen, television, phone, coffee/tea-making facilities, a balcony and a dining area. The interiors of the chalets are timber and they have been furnished in a simple, uncluttered way. Breakfast, served in the sunny dining room, is optional. Guests have a choice of Continental or European style, including cheeses and meats. As the chalets have been built into the side of a hill, some require a short walk down to the dining room. Ocean View Chalets are a favourite place to stay for guests embarking on adventures in Abel Tasman National Park where the native forests, beaches, clear waters, kayaking, hiking and all water activities are popular.

Accommodation available (NZ$)	👤	👤👤	+👤	🛏	🛁	Family dog on site Guest pets by arrangement
2 Studios	$108-128	$108-128		Q	EN	Breakfast: Extra $12.50pp
5 S/C cottages	$138-158	$138-158		Q	EN	
1 S/C cottage	$205-235	$205-235	$30	2Q	2EN	Guest rooms: Ambience: Setting/location:

ABEL TASMAN NATIONAL PARK - Tasman Bay - Nelson - Nelson Lakes - Marlborough Sounds - Blenheim - Kaikoura

100

Abel Tasman Marahau Lodge

Robyn and Don Caird
Marahau Beach Road, Marahau
Tel: 03 5278250
Fax: 03 5278258
robyn@abeltasmanmarahaulodge.co.nz
www.lodgings.co.nz – keyword: marahau

Property features
Native garden
Architecturally designed lodge
Rooms serviced
Sauna/spa pool/bbq/laundry
NZ Tourism Award finalist, 1999
Local features
Abel Tasman Nat Park-5 mins walk
Sea kayaking/seal swimming
Bush walks/local restaurants
Water taxis/beaches

Motueka - 20 mins drive
Nelson - 1 hour drive

From Nelson take SH 60. Follow
Abel Tasman National Park signs
after Motueka. At T junction to
Collingwood turn left, then hard right,
into Marahau Sandy Bay Rd. Lodge
is on left 500m before entry to park.

These semi-detached, modern chalets with Cathedral ceilings have the facilities of quality accommodation but with a more personal feel. Perfectly situated to enjoy the all day sun and access the native forests of the National Park and the beaches with beautiful clear water. Robyn and Don love it here and know their guests will also enjoy this little 'slice of paradise'. Breakfast although not included in the tariff, can be brought over to your chalet at the time you choose. Packed lunches are a popular request. For the studio chalets who do not have full kitchen facilities and who choose to "cook in" there is a communal kitchen where guests are often found swapping travel stories. Alternatively enjoy the local cuisine at either of the local licensed restaurants. There is also an outdoor barbecue, plus a spa and sauna for people to relax in after their energetic excursions in the Abel Tasman National Park. I loved the way the local water taxi works. Robyn booked it and all we had to do was jump in the boat, which was towed behind a tractor, when it stopped at the gate for us. We didn't even get our feet wet. The three acres of beautiful native gardens coupled with the excellent facilities also make the lodge ideal for conferences and functions.

Accommodation available (NZ$)	👤	👤👤	+👤	🛏	🛁
4 S/C units	$180-230	$180-230		SK+S	PR
8 Studio	$160	$160	$30	Q+S	EN

Breakfast: Extra $13pp

Guest rooms:
Ambience:
Setting/location:

LOW   HIGH

Packed lunches available upon request.

The Resurgence
Clare and Peter
Riwaka Valley Road, RD 3, Motueka
Tel: 03 5284664
Fax: 03 5284605
info@resurgence.co.nz
www.lodgings.co.nz – keyword: resurgence

Ⓟ ✉ ☎ ♿

MasterCard VISA

Property features
Swimming pool/spa pool
Bush walks and native birds
Fine dining with Nelson wines
Massages
Active & Gourmet short breaks
Local features
Abel Tasman National Park
Nelson Art & Wine trails
Golden Bay
Birding & Nature Tours
Kahurangi National Park

Marahau - 20 mins drive
Nelson Airport - 50 mins drive

Follow SH60 through Motueka,
Riwaka and past turnings for Abel
Tasman. In 2km, as SH60 starts to
rise, turn left into Riwaka Valley Roa
(blue LODGE sign). Continue 6km o
right branch.

The Resurgence set on 50 acres, faces the splendid hills of the Kahurangi National Park. The name Resurgence is taken from the nearby geological feature where the underground Riwaka River emerges from a marble landscape. Our hosts Clare and Peter took the time to show us the special features of the property that they are re-establishing with trees native to the area. A tree for every guest, what a wonderful way to share in the regeneration of this beautiful property. The lodge with its four guest rooms and the six self contained bush suites are all very spacious. The tasteful décor has been chosen to enhance the natural surroundings. We were encouraged to explore the network of bush tracks, enjoy the bird life and natural habitat, or visit the many nearby attractions of both the Abel Tasman and Kahurangi National Parks. After returning to the lodge we had the choice of a dip in the pool or the hot tub or alternatively you can book one of the many massage and therapeutic treatments on offer before joining fellow guests and the wonderful hosts for pre dinner drinks. The memorable four course dinner showcased the best of local produce, much of it coming from organic gardens on the property. Clare and Peter proudly support the Nelson-Tasman sustainable tourism charter. The Resurgence is the perfect place to spend a few days exploring this beautiful part of the Abel Tasman.

Accommodation available (NZ$)	🧍	🧍🧍	+🧍	🛏	🛁			
4 Rooms	$300-470	$375-545		Q	EN	Breakfast: Cooked		
3 S/C chalets	$325-395	$325-395		Q	EN	Evening meal: Included		
3 S/C lodges	$375-495	$375-495		SK or 2S	EN	Guest rooms:		
						Ambience:		
						Setting/location:		

Evening meals available. Main lodge rooms include pre dinner drinks, dinner and full cooked breakfast. Bush suites include hamper breakfast (full cooked @ $15pp)

LOW   HIC

Property features
Landscaped woodland garden
Grass tennis court/garden chess
Heated swimming pool
Next to 150 acre apple/pear orchard
Paeonies grown on site
CD player and fridge in rooms
Local features
Abel Tasman & Kahurangi parks
Golf courses/trout fishing
Beaches/kayaking
Wine & craft trails/next to vineyard

Motueka - 10 mins drive
Nelson - 40 mins drive

From Nelson travel towards Motueka
on SH 60. Weka Rd is the second
road on the left past Tasman Village.
Wairepo House entrance is approx.
200m along Weka Rd on the right.

Wairepo House

Joyanne and Richard Easton
Weka Road, Mariri, Coastal Highway, Nelson
Tel: 03 5266865   Mob: 021801044
Fax: 03 5266101
joyanne@wairepohouse.co.nz
www.lodgings.co.nz – keyword: wairepohouse

I drove through apple orchards and fields of peonies to arrive at Wairepo, which was a cheerful introduction to this stylish country home set in a meticulously landscaped garden, on a 150-acre orchard. Joyanne has created four comfortable suites in the house and entertains guests as if they were long-time friends. I loved the atmosphere; sophisticated but not the least bit pretentious. All the rooms are large, have a good deal of privacy, and open to the garden, the heated swimming pool or deck. There is a pizza oven by the pool for guest use. Joyanne also makes fresh bread in the oven for morning breakfast. To sleep here and wake up to the garden with its delightful abundance of flowers, silver beech and scarlett oak trees, to pass the tennis court and walk to the summer house or play chess with the life-size set, or petanque in the back garden was the perfect antidote to urban overload. I was there in the autumn and the trees were dressing in their reds and yellows. If weather had permitted, I would have had breakfast in the summerhouse or on the patio. But it was cool, and we ate in the dining room, which still visually includes the outdoors. Joyanne created a superb breakfast including meats and nuts, and choice of avocado, mozarello and bacon or pikelets, caramelized bananas, bacon and maple syrup - a hard choice.

Family dog on site

Breakfast: Special cooked

Guest rooms:
Ambience:
Setting/location:

Accommodation available (NZ$)	👤	👥	+👤	🛏	🛁
1 Suite	$365	$395	$55	SK	PR
1 Suite	$365	$395	$55	K	EN
1 Suite	$420	$450	$55	SK	EN
1 Suite	$520	$550	$55	SK + Q	EN
1 Suite	$620	$650	$55	Sk + SK/T	EN

Accent House

Wayne and Jacqui Rowe
148 Aranui Road, Mapua Village, Nelson
Tel: 03 5403442   Mob: 0275403442
Fax: 03 5403442   Free: 08005403442
info@accentbnb.co.nz
www.lodgings.co.nz – keyword: accenthouse

qualmark
★ ★ ★ ★ plus
guest & hosted

   12

Property features
Giant outdoor chess
Petanque/free internet
Private guest entrance/lounge
Off street parking
Spacious grounds
Local features
Jet boating/Tours/Mapua Village
Able Tasman National Park
Nelson City - 30 mins drive
Nelson Airport - 15 mins drive
Walk to local restaurants

Nelson - 30 mins drive
Motueka - 10 mins drive

From Nelson, Richmond and Westport; follow SH6 until you reach the large round-about which joins SH60. Stay on SH60. Turn right at Mapua School into Aranui Rd and the Accent House is located opposite Aranui Park.

The coastal village of Mapua in heart of Tasman Bay has long been renowned for fish cafés, art galleries and it picturesque setting. Accent house is a new addition to this list. Jacqui and Wayne have established their beautiful award winning home just off highway 60. Sweep into the driveway past the expansive, newly planted gardens to the front entrance, Jacqui greeted us and showed us to our room, one of three guest rooms which is tastefully decorated using restful colours and the finest of linens. The ensuite bathrooms are all luxurious with personal touches and soft towels. Retiring to the guest lounge proved to be a haven for weary travellers with every convenience. Fully rested, fine dining at breakfast takes on a new meaning, with an exquisite table setting, and delicious breakfast options, We set off to explore the surroundings. The choice's are limitless, local wineries, art galleries, kayaking, a stroll down the path and along the shorefront to the estuary, golf, outdoor chess /petanque or Abel Tasman National Park, The galleries won, after which relaxing on the deck overlooking the pond with a glass of the finest local wine, and the last of the sun going down on our faces seemed the perfect way to end the day. Maybe Abel Tasman National Park tomorrow.

Accommodation available (NZ$)	👤	👥	+👤	🛏	🛁
3 rooms	$185-225	$185-225	Q	EN	Breakfast: Cooked/continental

Affordable luxury, guest laundry fully equipt.

Guest rooms:
Ambience:
Setting/location:

LOW   HIG

Property features
Stunning 360 degree views
Peaceful and private country stay
High speed internet
Comfortable guest lounge
Petanque and croquet
Local features
Restaurants/wineries/village - 6 mins
Two golf courses - 10 mins drive
Golf clubs for loan
Personalised day trips organised
In the centre of Nelson Provence

Clayridge House
Marion and Peter Copp
77 Pine Hill Road, Ruby Bay, Nelson
Tel: 03 5402548   Mob: 0274472099
Fax: 03 5402541
info@clayridge.co.nz
www.lodgings.co.nz – keyword: clayridge

Motueka - 15 mins drive
Nelson - 25 mins drive

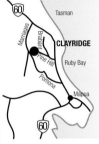

From Richmond drive 20 mins
towards Motueka on SH60. At
Ruby Bay, drive 100m past Ruby
Bay store, turn left Pine Hill Rd.
Clayridge House sign is 0.5 km
on left.

Located high on a ridge above Nelson's popular Ruby Bay and the quaint seaside village of Mapua, Clayridge House has spectacular 360-degree views. From almost anywhere on the property, I was able to admire the wide blue expanse of Tasman Bay with Nelson city and Rabbit Island in the distance. Inland, the view is across rolling pasture, orchards, vineyards and small lakes to the distant mountains. You can watch this ever-changing picture-postcard view from either of Clayridge's two immaculate, ultra-modern, self-contained cottages. Each has two bedrooms. A shell pathway meanders to the nearby home of hosts, Marion and Peter Copp, where a further bedroom (with ensuite) is available for bed and breakfast guests. Both Marion and Peter have creative interests. Marion is a keen photographer, Peter is a hobby artist and many of their fine works are on display. Breakfast, was a sumptuous affair served at a sunny table. Wide, corner-opening windows in the room let in the fresh air and allowed a good view of the rose gardens where some 90-odd varieties grow. I could also have been served outside if the weather was right or in the dining room. Guests mingle in a spacious guest lounge with an open fireplace and comfortable leather couches.

Family pets on site
Guest pets by arrangement

Accommodation available (NZ$)	♂	♂♂	+♂	🛏	🛁
Breakfast: Cooked					
1 Room	$150	$250		SK or 2KS	EN
2 Cottages	$180	$180	$30	K+Q	PR

Guest rooms:
Ambience:
Setting/location:

LOW   HIGH

Cottages are 5 star Qualmark graded and have a breakfast option available - extra charge.

Bronte Lodge

Daniel Fraser
Bronte Road East, Off Coastal Highway 60, near Mapua
Tel: 03 5402422   Mob: 021540988
Fax: 03 5402637
stay@brontelodge.co.nz
www.lodgings.co.nz – keyword: bronte

(P) ✉ 🖨 (📞) ♿

Property features
Petanque/tennis court
Historic setting/estuary shoreline
Airport pick-up available: $60
Dinghy/canoe/mountain bikes
Gardens/boutique vineyard
Heated saltwater lap pool
Local features
Wineries/arts & crafts
Abel Tasman National Park
Nearby beaches/golf course
Award winning restaurants

Nelson - 30 mins drive
Richmond - 15 mins drive

Turn onto SH 60 from SH 6 on the southern side of Richmond. Travel for approx. 10 minutes along Coastal Hwy 60 to Bronte Road East. Turn right into this road and travel 1.5km to the gate.

The water at high tide lapped just feet away from the deck of my secluded hideaway. Five luxury units sit on the water's edge, each with private decks and magnificent views of the Waimea Inlet. It is quiet and peaceful, and yet only 30 minutes from Nelson. Margaret and Bruce seem to have thought of everything when they designed the interiors of these suites and villas. They are modern, crisp and stylish, with a relaxing ambience and lack nothing in detail including robes, local art, binoculars, pre dinner drinks, cookies and an extensive range of bathroom extras. Each contains a king-size bed, kitchenette, comfortable living space with lounge chairs and coffee table. The bathroom is modern and built for luxury. After a day's adventure you can soak any stress away in the spa bath or enjoy a Chardonnay on the deck, listening to the lapping water and songbirds at sunset. Breakfast is special at Bronte – the food and the setting. The diverse menu may include local fruit juices, croissants, a variety of waffles and omelettes, free-range eggs and the freshest local fruits; and espresso made from locally roasted beans. Bronte has its own small vineyard, a 13-metre heated swimming pool and a tennis court.

Accommodation available (NZ$)	👤	👥	+👤	🛏	🛁	Family pets on site
1 Suite	$480	$495		K	EN	Breakfast: Cooked
1 Suite	$480	$495		SK/T	EN	
1 Suite	$580	$595		K	EN	Guest rooms:
1 Suite	$580	$595		SK/T	EN	Ambience:
1 S/C villa		$695	$50	K+SK/T	EN	Setting/location:
		(4 persons)				

LOW   HIGH

Property features
Farm and Woodland walk
Birdwatching
Rowing boat on lake
Views to lake/farmland/mountains
Secluded peaceful location
Local features
Walks/wineries/arts/crafts
Beaches/golf courses nearby
Abel Tasman National Park
Kahurangi National Park

Aporo Pondsiders
Marian and Mike Day
Permin Road, Tasman, Nelson
Tel: 03 5266858   Mob: 0272403757
Fax: 03 5266258
marian@aporo.co.nz
www.lodgings.co.nz – keyword: aporopondsiders

Motueka - 10 mins drive
Nelson - 30 mins drive

From Nelson travel on SH 6, turn
onto SH 60. Travel approx 20
mins. Turn right into Permin Road.
Aporo's drive is first left.

As I left the main road I wondered what I might find and discovered, to my delight, three very chic modern villas built literally over an ornamental pond. Marian welcomed me aboard. How cool and pleasant it was walking onto the decking and into the pondsider. The next best thing to being on a boat, except no rocking. Each villa has been cleverly staggered to give privacy. From the balconies, which are accessed from large sliding doors, you can watch the bird life, ducks cruising in and out of the rushes, or the views of mountains and farmland. Marian and Mike have planted many native shrubs and trees to enhance the pond. The interiors, carefully chosen, give a very contemporary feeling, using fabrics, textures and colour in great harmony. Underfloor heating and all the latest equipment for easy living is here. Interesting hamper breakfasts or provisions are provided. The fresh fruit and flowers, homebaking and port just topped it off. I was delighted by all that has been achieved here. This place is very near the Abel Tasman National Park and only 30 minutes from Nelson. A very central spot for all this region has to offer.

Accommodation available (NZ$)	♦	♦♦	+♦	🛏	🛁
2 S/C cottage	$300		$40	K	EN
1 S/C cottage	$300		$70	K	PR

Breakfast: Special cooked

Guest rooms:
Ambience:
Setting/location:

LOW   HIGH

All cottages have kitchen facilities.

Villa 10 Waterfront Apartments

Jenny Burton and Graham Snadden
10 Richardson St, Nelson
Tel: 03 5484619
Fax: 03 5456110
info@villa10.co.nz
www.lodgings.co.nz – keyword: villa10

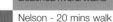

Property features
Stunning sea and mountain views
Beautifully restored colonial villa
Private verandahs
Original work by local artists
Jenny's handpaints textiles
Highspeed wireless connection
Local features
Walk to waterfront cafes - 5 mins
Arts/crafts/galleries/vineyards
Easy access to three National Parks
Beaches/rivers/walks

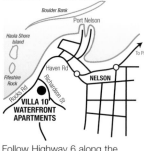

Nelson - 20 mins walk
Blenheim - 2 hour drive

Follow Highway 6 along the waterfront. Turn up the hill into Richardson Street at the intersection opposite Haulashore Island and the Harbour entrance. Villa 10 is signposted, second on the right.

Jenny and Graham have done a fantastic job converting their large family home, built in 1908, into two separate, self-contained villas. Both have unobstructed views out to Haulashore Island and beautiful Tasman Bay. The Loft, which is the upstairs villa, is ideal for a couple looking for romance. The walls reflect the colour of the sea, and bold, coloured textiles, made by Jenny, add to the ocean theme. I really enjoyed this place; the attention to detail and comfort as well as the views. The Loft has a king-size bed, which is overhung by an amazing canopy imprinted with glowing stars. The Westwing Villa, which has been kept in its original form, is decorated with warm colours and has two generous-sized rooms that lead onto a Victorian verandah. Even relaxing in the bath, I could still see the view. Both villas are filled with original art and many of Jenny's own creations. They are fully self-contained but instead of eating in, I walked down to the waterfront where I found many award-winning restaurants. And there was no need to worry about stocking up for breakfast. The pantry and fridge in the villas were filled with a variety of fresh produce for breakfast.

Accommodation available (NZ$)	🧍	🧍🧍	+🧍	🛏	🛁	
1S/C Apartment	$215-255	$215-255	$25	Q+2S	PR	Breakfast: Provisions provided
1S/C Apartment	$215-255	$215-255	$25	K+D	PR	

Guest rooms:
Ambience:
Setting/location:

LOW   HIGH

Minimum stay 2 nights. Kitchen/breakfast provisions.

Property features
Spectacular views of harbour & bay
Quiet bush surroundings
Privacy and total independence
Private BBQ area/deck
Mountain bikes avail
Décor with nautical theme
Local features
Pottery & craft galleries
Beaches/walks
Abel Tasman National Park
Vineyards/wineries

The Wheelhouse Inn
Ralph and Sally Hetzel
41 Whitby Road, Nelson
Tel: 03 5468391   Mob: 021901991
Fax: 03 5468393
wheelhouse@ts.co.nz
www.lodgings.co.nz – keyword: wheelhouse

Nelson - 5 mins drive
Motueka - 40 mins drive

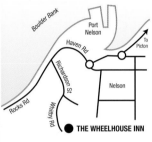

● THE WHEELHOUSE INN

From Nelson drive towards
Tahunanui via waterfront (Rocks Rd).
About halfway between the port &
Tahunanui turn left up Richardson
St. Go straight ahead on to Whitby
Rd - continue to end.

    This view took my breath away. In this highly elevated position, the outlook over Tasman Bay is magic. The Wheelhouse Inn accommodation consists of five individual holiday homes. The Wheelhouse and the Chart House Main Deck have one bedroom while the Captain's Quarters, The Crow's Nest and the Chart House Upper Deck are all two bedrooms. These modern homes have large fronts that are mostly glass so there is no shortage of light or access to the view. With the skilled use of timber and quality furnishings, the décor is comfortable and uncluttered. The nautical theme using pictures and old boating paraphernalia adds interest, even for landlubbers. All houses have well-equipped, kitchens and lounges with great views, televisions, CD players, DVD's and broadband internet. The wonderful decks are perfect for those BBQ's and relaxing with one of the local wines in hand taking in the sun and the stunning vista. The wonderful hosts live up the drive, but they make an effort not to interrupt your stay but are only a moment away if you require assistance. Just five minutes from the heart of Nelson and located up on a hill that is surrounded by trees and shrubs, it is very peaceful however the cafes on the waterfront are only a short distance away. That is if you are able to tear yourself away from your glorious nest on the hillside.

Accommodation available (NZ$)	👤	👤👤	+👤	🛏	🛁
1 S/C house	$130-190	$130-190	$15	Q+S	PR
1 S/C house	$130-190	$130-190	$15	Q+2S	PR
1 S/C house	$130-190	$130-190	$15	Q+2S	PR
1 S/C house	$130-190	$130-190	$15	K	PR
1 S/C house	$130-190	$130-190	$15	K+2S	PR

Breakfast: Extra $15pp

Guest rooms:
Ambience:
Setting/location:

LOW   HIGH

109

The Little Retreat

Angela Higgins
Level 1/ 22 Nile St West, Nelson
Tel: 03 5451411   Mob: 0212471891
Fax: 03 5451417
the.little.retreat@xtra.co.nz
www.lodgings.co.nz – keyword: littleretreat

(P) 👣 ✉ 📺 📞

Property features
Fully self contained mod urban
Inner city retreat above health centre
Quiet/views/two balconies/BBQ
All day sun/spabath/central heating
Local features
Art/pottery/glass galleries
Restaurants/café/shops 2 mins
Beaches/wineries/museum
WOW centre/gardens
Abel Tasman National Park
Golf courses

Nelson CBD - 2 min walk
Richmond - 15 mins drive

Bridge St
Trafalgar St
Hardy St
Selwyn Pl
Rutherford St
Nile St West
South St
Christ Church Cathedral
Collingwood St
THE LITTLE RETREAT

From Nelson's main street, Trafalger St, turn right at the church steps, then first left, then first right onto Nile St West. The Little Retreat is at No 2 opposite the Rutherford Hotel.

"A Little Retreat indeed" and "Little piece of paradise" are both quotes I read from the guest book. Located in the heart of Nelson with views of the Nelson Cathedral is a well appointed apartment. Ideally situated above a natural health centre called Being which is run by the host Angela. It is only a short few minutes stroll into town. The decor is ultra-modern with up-to-the-minute amenities and a fully equipped kitchen and laundry. The Little Retreat has one bedroom with a king-size bed, spa bath and other luxuries such as bathrobes and nice toiletries. There is also a day bed in the living room for an extra guest or a place to relax while watching the LCD television. There are two private decks, one with a barbeque. I spent my first day at the retreat reading quietly, and then booked myself in for a soothing shiatsu massage downstairs at Being. As I was there on a Sunday I awoke to the ringing of bells from the Cathedral. I sat on the front deck and watched people pass by on their way to church or to the various activities in the town. Angela had left me provisions, including fresh fruit, breads and eggs etc. and enjoyed breakfast al fresco while I warmed myself in the sun.

Accommodation available (NZ$)	👤	👤👤	+👤	🛏	🛁	
1 S/C unit	$195	$195-240	$25	K+Q	PR	Breakfast: Provisions provided

Guest rooms:
Ambience:
Setting/location:

LOW   HIGH

Property features
Quiet yet close to city centre
Heat pumps/air conditioning
Interior design includes local art
Guest lounge/CD/VCR/books
English garden/pond/seating
Suite has a kitchenette
Local features
Walk to restaurants/cafes
Art & craft galleries/vineyards
City/bush walks
Beaches & public gardens

Shelbourne Villa
Val and Wayne Ballantyne
21 Shelbourne Street, Nelson
Tel: 03 5459059   Mob: 0274474186
Fax: 03 5467248
beds@shelbournevilla.co.nz
www.lodgings.co.nz – keyword: shelbourne

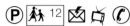

Nelson - 5 mins walk
Picton - 2 hours

From SH 6 drive down Trafalgar St
(main street in town centre) towards
the cathedral. Take the last road
left (Selwyn Pl) then second right
(Shelbourne St). Shelbourne Villa is
number 21 on your left.

This adapted villa, recently taken over by Val and Wayne, is tucked away in a quiet corner of Nelson, just five minutes walk from the city centre. The designed wood and metal gates opening to the property are an indication of the theme of the house which is decorated and furnished with the work of local artists, many of whom live nearby. I could have wallowed in the comfort of the guest lounge and admired its leafy outlook, but I preferred to wander the house and garden to find among the sculptures, paintings and ceramics, works from Jane Evans, Grant Palliser, Bill Burke and Christine Boswijk. The upstairs suite with a balcony and view over the town is furnished in a slick contemporary style incorporating the excellent metal designs of Glenn van der Leij. Of particular note are the geometric fireplace surround and the innovative wardrobe. The three other rooms, two at ground level and one downstairs are very spacious with sleigh beds, writing desks, televisions, lounge chairs, stocked bookshelves, art work and extra-large ensuites all immaculately presented. The large colourful garden is dominated by birch trees and has several attractive sitting areas on different levels.

Accommodation available (NZ$)	👤	👥	+👤	🛏	🛁
Breakfast: Cooked					
1 Room	$225	$245		K	EN
1 Room	$275	$295		K	EN
Guest rooms:					
1 Room	$345	$365		SK	EN
Ambience:	1 Suite	$240	$260	$50	K	EN
Setting/location:					

A Culinary Experience

Joe Waller and Kay Pastorius
71 Tresillian Avenue, Atawhai, Nelson
Tel: 03 5451886   Mob: 0274451886
Fax: 03 5451869   Free: 0800891886
kpastorius@xtra.co.nz
www.lodgings.co.nz – keyword: culinary

Property features
Homemade pastries on arrival
In house chef and masseuse
Cooking classes/gourmet meals
Sculpture garden
Large art collection
Local features
Three national parks
Wineries/arts and crafts/markets
Award-winning cafes
Boating/fishing/kayaking
Golf/beaches/tramping

Nelson - 7 mins drive
Picton - 1 hr 45 mins drive

6km north of Nelson city, turn right on Marybank Road. There is a sign "B&B 600m". Turn left on Jackson and right on Tresillian. A Culinary Experience is on the right.

The name says it all. A stay with Kay and Joe will leave you totally relaxed and full of fresh ideas in the kitchen! Kay previously owned the School of International Cuisine in Laguna Beach, California, provides gourmet dinners and teaches cooking classes on request. Kay and Joe, delightful and entertaining hosts welcomed me and we chatted over drinks and superb chocolate cookies. Their home reflects their many travels with an outstanding collection of art pieces. I spent sometime just taking it all in. Kay and Joe continue the European theme in the guest rooms - the Chambre de Provence is decorated with French art and linen, and the Tuscan Room features Italian art and linen. Indulge with a soak in the spa enjoying the view of Nelson's Boulder Bank followed by a therapeutic massage. Joe is a certified naturopathic doctor. Kay's breakfasts are legendary, blueberry pancakes, omelettes, salmon, fruits and cereals. Try her own cheese and Herbs de Provence, delicious! Its just a short drive to the centre of Nelson, for galleries, restaurants and museums. There is so much to do here that A culinary package holiday – A Pampered Weekend and the Indulgence Holiday seemed a must. I truly felt pampered and wished that like their delightful Yorkshire terrier I could experience this kind of hospitality every day.

Accommodation available (NZ$)	👤	👤👤	+👤	🛏	🛁	Guest pets by arrangement
2 Rooms	$160-260	$175-275		SK/T	EN	Breakfast: Special cooked

Evening meal: $75pp
Guest rooms:
Ambience:
Setting/location:

Property features
Colonial architecture
Swimming pool/spa pool
Separate guest lounge/dining
Complimentary refreshments
Mature garden with sea views
Local features
Vineyards/wineries
Art/craft galleries
Three National parks
Restaurants/cafes - 5 mins
Golf course/beaches/walks

Muritai Manor
Alex and Julia Hunter
48 Wakapuaka Road, Wakapuaka RD 1, Nelson
Tel: 03 5451189   Mob: 0211067737
Fax: 03 5450740   Free: 0800260262
stay@muritaimanor.co.nz
www.lodgings.co.nz – keyword: muritaimanor

Nelson - 5 mins drive
Blenheim - 1 hr 30 mins drive

From Nelson, take SH 6 towards
Blenheim. Travel for approx. 5
mins. Muritai Manor is on the right
after Clifton Terrace school and
Allisdair St.

If you drive toward Picton from Nelson for five minutes you will arrive at this impressive example of colonial architecture. Climbing roses cover the balconies, and established trees in the large garden provide shelter and shade. Muritai Manor was built in 1903, and some years ago was converted to a bed and breakfast. The renovations are sympathetic to the original design. Heavy drapes in the front guestrooms frame the view through the sash windows of Nelson Haven, Abel Tasman National Park and Rabbit Island. Other rooms have views over the swimming pool with some harbour and rural views. Thoughtful touches in the guestrooms such as flowers, chocolates, and herbal teas and the table/desk and chair for writing letters home (or maybe work) make it clear that this is more than just a business for the hosts. I am sure that other guests appreciate their efforts as much as I did. The formal dining room and guest living areas offer the same style and comfort. Even though it is an older home I found Muritai Manor to be bright and sunny and a very pleasant place to stay.

Family pets on site

Breakfast: Special cooked

Guest rooms:
Ambience:
Setting/location:

Accommodation available (NZ$)	♦	♦♦	+♦	🛏	🛁
2 Rooms	$220	$245		Q	EN
1 Room	$230	$275		K	EN
1 Room	$230	$275		SK/T	EN
1 Cottage	$260	$310	$75	SK/T +S	EN

Tira Ora Estate

Tony and Annebeth Broad
North West Bay, Pelorus Sound, Marlborough
Tel: 03 5798117
Fax: 03 5798116
stay@tira-ora-estate.com
www.lodgings.co.nz – keyword: tiraora

Property features
Privacy/seclusion/isolation
Open fire/sea views
Hammocks/bush walks
Outdoor bath/sauna/spa pool
Animals and bird life
Kayaks/horse riding
Beach/swimming
Bush hiking
Local features
Fishing charters/fishing
Scenic Sounds

Havelock - 45 mins by boat
Wellington - 20 mins flight

Tira Ora Estate can only be reached by water taxi from Havelock or by plane: the property has a grass landing strip.

This is not for the faint hearted. Tira Ora Estate is either reached via aircraft from Wellington or a 45 minute water taxi from the Havelock marina. North West Bay is situated in a very spectacular part of the Pelorus Sound. Stepping ashore and heading up the driveway to the main lodge it is not long before one gets the impression that this is indeed a relaxed and carefree retreat. The no frills rooms are situated in pairs a short distance from the main lodge which was part of the original homestead. This Christian family have developed a unique haven of animals and bird life including black sheep, ostrich that will sit and let you stroke them, llamas, donkeys, horses and of course the friendly collection of dogs. For the water enthusiastic, there are kayaks and jet skis and for the less adventurous just relaxing at the lodge is an option. The extensive library has an array of modern and historical books from religious studies to art and music. My choice was taking time out just sitting in a chair at the beach gazebo just watching the changing scenery in the sounds. Maybe tomorrow I might take a picnic lunch and head for the "stairway to heaven" a ridge high above the lodge or maybe one of the secluded retreats on the property. This is a place for families to get back to nature and family values.

Accommodation available (NZ$)			+			Family pets on site Guest pets by arrangement
2 Rooms	$250-300	$450-600	Q	EN		Breakfast: Special cooked
1 Room	$250-300	$450-600	D+S	EN		Evening meal: Included
2 Rooms	$250-300	$450-600	Q+S	EN		Guest rooms: Ambience: Setting/location:

Extra beds available for families. All meals are included in the tariffs.

LOW   HIGH

Property features
Stunning sea views
Swimming pool/spa pool
Guest lounge & dining
Kayaks & bikes on site
Blist'd foot café (lunch)
Local features
Queen Charlotte walkway - 5 mins
Marlborough vineyards - 40 mins
Sea plane flights available
Mussel boat trip/mail boat cruise
Horse riding/goldmine walk

Tirimoana House Luxury B&B
John and Michelle Hotham
257 Anakiwa Road, RD 1, Picton
Tel: 03 5742627   Mob: 0211672342
Fax: 03 5742647
bookings@tirimoanahouse.com
www.lodgings.co.nz – keyword: tirimoana

Picton - 30 mins drive
Blenheim - 40 mins drive

From Blenheim/Nelson drive to
Havelock, turn at the large Queen
Charlotte Drive sign. Continue pass
Linkwater (petrol station) until the large
Queen Charlotte Walkway sign, turn
into Anakiwa road continue for 5 mins.
Tirimoana house is on your left.

Just thirty minutes from Picton, perched on the upper reaches of the Queen Charlotte Sound there is Tirimoana House. New Zealand hosts John and Michelle have transformed this beach front accommodation into a stunning bed and breakfast. After six years of travelling and life in the city Michelle, a qualified chef and John have embraced life in The Sounds. Tirimoana House has three exquisitely furnished, ensuite rooms and a separate suite appropriately named the Queen Charlotte. However it is hard to be prepared for the overwhelming "wow" factor on entering their premier room the "Sunrise" Should I rush out onto the deck and admire the view over the idyllic inlet or take in the furnishings. Some furniture, the bedroom features a queen size four poster, carved bed originally used by senior officers of the East India Company. The linen as in all the rooms is luxurious and sensual. However it wasn't long before we were joining our hosts for a pre dinner drink. John and Michelle are excellent hosts and amidst much laughter, great food and local wines we planned the next few days. Walk the Queen Charlotte track, sea kayak the many inlets, take a tour to the renowned Marlborough vineyards, or simply do nothing at all. Take a book, relax by the pool. I could not help agree with them – this is the life.

Family dog on site

Accommodation available (NZ$)					

Breakfast: Cooked
Evening meal: $40-$50pp
Guest rooms:
Ambience:
Setting/location:

2 Rooms	$160-180		Q	EN
1 Room	$250-260		Q	EN
1 Suite	$260-300	$80	Q	EN

Please enquire for single tariff rates. Iron, hair dryer, laptop and laundry facilities available. Additional beds available in suite upon request.

Sherrington Grange

Lisa & Julie Harper
Mahau Sound, RD 2, Picton
Tel: 03 5742655
Fax: 03 5742655
info@sherringtongrange.co.nz
www.lodgings.co.nz – keyword: sherringtongrange

Property features
Antique/art/muscial instruments
400 acres with private wharf
2km deserted coastline
Over 10km walking tracks
Cheese & honey made on site
Local features
Area of great natural beauty
Boat trips - 5 min drive
Queen Charlotte track - 10 min drive
Wineries - 50 min drive

Picton - 50 mins drive
Blenheim - 50 mins drive

Turn up Kenepuru Road at Linkwate
and after approx 20 minutes, take th
signposted driveway (first road after
the cattle stop).

Just under an hours drive from Picton, the Harper Family Farm sits on Mahau Sound. Turn off the Picton-Havelock road heading toward Kenepuru, about 20 minutes along just after the first cattle stop, there's a "Sherrington" sign directing one down Mahau road. To city dwellers this appears little more than a farm track. It is. And that's the point. Whilst very definitely a lodge and not a farm stay guests delight in being shown Lisa's artisan cheese making. Another intriguing endeavour is beekeeping. There's 400 acres of farm, so plenty of walking to be done, and with over 2 kilometers of coastline to share with fellow guests, one can be assured of quiet spot by the sea. Something a little more active? The sounds are relatively kayak friendly. Fishing is great too. Possibly because there's not much competition! But the appeal here is of a real get away to a family atmosphere. Farm meals are made memorable by proper attention to superb product, a lot of which comes from the farm itself. Special diet? "Absolutely not a problem" says Lisa. "We are fully equipped and trained accordingly". So why Sherrington? For its isolation and the tranquillity, for the family guest experience and for the farm products involvement.

Accommodation available (NZ$)	🧍	🧍🧍	+🧍	🛏	🛁	Family pets on site
1 Room	$120	$150		Q	GS	
1 Room	$140	$180	$40	SK	GS	

Breakfast: Special continental
Evening meal: $35pp
Guest rooms:
Ambience:
Setting/location:

LOW   HIGH

Property features
Waterfront location
Kayaking
Spa pool
Private bar
Walking tracks
Boating activities
Local features
Historical attractions
Mussel farming tours
Whale and Dolphin watching
Bird life

Picton - 25 mins drive
Blenheim - 60 mins drive

From Picton take the Port
Underwood Rd, continue through
Whatamonga Bay settlement, then
follow the Blenheim Rd to
Oyster Bay Lodge.

Oyster Bay Lodge
Raewyn and Rob Kirkwood
1474 Port Underwood Road, Oyster Bay,
Marlborough Sounds
Tel: 03 5799644   Mob: 0274363363
Fax: 03 5799645
enquiries@oysterbaylodge.co.nz
www.lodgings.co.nz – keyword: oysterbay

Venture east out of Picton over the hills on a well constructed but windy road toward Port Underwood. Care is required, but rewarded, as one climbs to over 500 meters. Be sure to pull-off at the lookout, affording magnificent sounds vistas. It's only 19 kilometers to Oyster Bay. Allow time to appreciate the bush hills and those views! Descending into the bay, there's a tiny port servicing local aquaculture and fishing. Oyster Bay Lodge nestles into a rise on the sunny side overlooking the wharf. Aside from the odd mussel truck, taking marine produce to market, it's unlikely one will pass more than one or two cars. Raewyn and Rob's purpose developed lodge caters to those enjoying on-water activities. Learn to kayak in the safety of the Bay. Rob or Raewyn will take you on a cruise unravelling the areas coves, bays and inlets with commentary on the history. And what a history! From whaling to aquaculture, from Te Rauparaha to the Colonist. Complete your day with a luxury spa or take a seat on the lodges expansive decks with a glass of Marlborough wine and watch the sun slide behind the hills. Surely dinner has to be local mussels, the Sounds famous blue cod or maybe the areas well known venison? There is so much to do, one night is not enough.

	Accommodation available (NZ$)	🧍	🧍🧍	+🧍	🛏	🛁
Family cat on site						
Breakfast: Cooked	1 Room	$150	$180		K	EN
Evening meal: $60pp	1 Room	$150	$180		Q	PR
Guest rooms:	1 Room	$150	$180		2S	PR
Ambience:	1S/C apartment		$160-190		Q+D+S	PR
Setting/location:						

LOW   HIGH

117

Jefferswood

Jeff and Sandra Sewell
Cameron Road, RD1, Havelock, Marlborough
Tel: 03 5728081
Fax: 03 5728091
jefferswood.sewell@xtra.co.nz
www.lodgings.co.nz – keyword: jefferswood

(P) ✉ ♿

MasterCard VISA

Property features
Arboretum and pond
Native birds and bush views
Adobe/schist homestead
Organic orchard/gardens
Easy going hosts
Local features
Havelock township & marina
Marlborough Sounds
Queen Charlotte Track
Trout fishing
Wineries

Havelock - 15 min drive
Picton via Rapaura Rd - 40 mins drive

From Nelson pass through Havelock,
continue driving south down SH6
for 10 minutes. Pass the Okaramio
Hotel on your left. Drive 1km, turn into
Camerons Rd on right. Jefferswood is
300m (on shingle).

Jefferswood is a unique eco-friendly adobe homestead, set on four hectares of rural splendour between Blenheim and Havelock. I easily found the Jefferswood sign and followed it down the shingle road off SH 6. Turning into a driveway lined with handsome Plane trees I pulled up to the homestead and was struck by the warmth of the Adobe construction. Sandra greeted me at the front entrance to show me to my comfortable room, with a sumptuous bed, pampering ensuite, huge walk-in shower and abundant solar heated water. I then shared in a welcoming afternoon tea where I indulged in homemade fruitcake and biscuits, yum! I decided to have a stretch, so went for a stroll around the extensive property to look at the arboretum, organic orchard and large vegetable garden. I could not help but sneak into the garden and help myself to a few juicy sweet cocktail tomatoes. Bird life is very abundant at Jefferswood. I relaxed in the lounge room in front of an enormous picture window, and enjoyed a glass of Marlborough wine and nibbles, then later dined at the local café in Havelock on the marina, and watched several boats launching on the slip. A blissful night's sleep was followed by a home made breakfast of pancakes served with a fresh berry sauce, fresh pressed juices and brewed coffee. Treat yourself to the experience.

Accommodation available (NZ$)	🧍	🧍🧍	+🧍	🛏	🛁	Guest pets by arrangement
1 Room	$185	$240		Q	EN	Breakfast: Special cooked
1 Room	$185	$240		SK or 2S	EN	

Guest rooms:
Ambience:
Setting/location:

LOW   HIGH

Property features
1886 Heritage-registered villa
5 acre private bush & garden setting
Short stroll to Picton's amenities
Luxurious character apartments
Courtesy transfers/internet

Local features
Queen Charlotte track & cruises
Marlborough vineyard tours
Dolphin/bird/eco tours
Gift shops/restaurants/beaches
Sailing/kayaking/mountain biking

Sennen House

Richard and Imogen Fawcett
9 Oxford Street, Picton, Marlborough
Tel: 03 5735216   Mob: 0210359956
Fax: 03 5735216
enquiries@sennenhouse.co.nz
www.lodgings.co.nz – keyword: sennen

Picton - 5 mins walk
Blenheim - 20 mins drive

Oxford Street runs off Nelson
Square in Picton.

Here's a magnificent piece of New Zealand history! The house, built in 1886 sits on 5 acres of bush backdrop within walking distance of Picton's café's and restaurants. Old established plantings frame this heritage registered home adding to the established aura of ambience impossible to attain in today's constructions. Richard and Imogen restored and combined the very best of historic charm and contemporary style. Yes, there are screens, DVD players, computer availability. It's all there, but unobtrusively. Doors, locks, hinges, knobs and exquisite native timbers complete the restoration The Historic theme continues, the five rooms James Cook, Queen Victoria, Sir Joseph Banks, Queen Charlotte and Edwin Fox are all as individual as their personalities. Sumptuous linens, rich colours, nothing has been spared, and all have kitchens, dining areas and views of the hills and out over Picton to the sea beyond. We joined Richard and Imogen who live at the entrance to the property in an early colonial cottage appropriately named "The Gatehouse" for evening drinks and planned another day of exploring the sounds and the Marlborough wine growing district. Sennen House, so close to Picton Ferry is a great introduction to Marlborough.

Family cat on site

Breakfast: Special continental

Guest rooms:
Ambience:
Setting/location:

Accommodation available (NZ$)	🧍	🧍🧍	+🧍	🛏	🛁
1 Room	$280-300	$325-345		Q	EN
1 Room	$300-330	$345-375	$75	Q+S	EN
1 Room	$300-330	$345-375	$75	K	EN
1 Room	$350-380	$395-425	$75	K	EN
1 Room	$400-430	$445-475	$75	SK or 2S	EN

119

Owen River Lodge

Felix Borenstein
Owen Valley East Road, Murchison, Nelson Lakes
Tel: 03 5239075
Fax: 03 5239076
stay@owenriverlodge.co.nz
www.lodgings.co.nz – keyword: owenriver

(P) 🚶 12 ✉

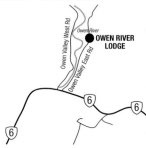

Property features
2 lounge areas/TV/video player/DVD
Onsite chef
On-site fly fishing equipment
Absolute river frontage
16 acres of gardens/farmland
Surrounded by National Park
Local features
Golf/horse riding/wine tasting
Rafting/canoeing/tramping/hiking
Cycling/mountain biking/fishing
Hot air ballooning/skydiving/gliding

Murchison - 15 mins drive
Nelson - 1.5 hour drive

From Nelson, drive south on SH 6 towards Murchison. Approx 110 kms from Nelson turn right into Owen Valle East Road (before Owen River Bridge Lodge is 2 kms down rd on left.

Check it out - even the smallest map shows Owen River as a destination. Only 15 mins from Murchison and the Nelson Lakes nearby, Owen River Lodge, is certainly a destination. Drive up and Felix is there to greet you. The aroma of home baking and coffee drifts from the lodge. His enthusiasm is infectious as we are shown around the lodge. Fishing boots, waders, rods are all here and of the highest quality. There are countless fishing spots with in a 40 minute drive, some right at your feet. Alternatively there are mountain bikes for exploring the terrain leading to Mt Owen Range. Something more relaxed, then there is the massage room and spa overlooking the river. Fishing you might think that this is it, but really Owen River Lodge is about people. Join the fantastic staff for pre-dinner drinks around the fireplace, followed by a four course dinner utlising the best of organic produce from the garden accompanied by Marlborough wines. Felix, the entertainment director encouraged us to share stories and plan our days. The six spacious rooms, in a separate wing are all beautifully decorated with top quality linens and furnishings. Fresh flowers from the garden and luxurious toiletries add the personal touch. Owen River Lodge is certainly a place to enjoy nature at its best but is also a great place to chill out, take a massage, read a book and make new friends.

Accommodation available (NZ$)	🧍	🧍🧍	+🧍	🛏	🛁
6 Rooms	$450	$780		SK or 2S	EN

Breakfast: Special cooked
Evening meal: Included
Guest rooms:
Ambience:
Setting/location:

LOW   HIGI

Property features
Includes glass of Le Grys wine
Mudblock construction
Indoor solar heated swimming pool
Vineyard setting

Local features
Vineyards/wineries/olive groves
Trout fishing
Horse and trap winery tours
Sailing/mailboat trips
Golf courses
Horse riding/walks

Blenheim - 15 mins drive
Picton - 25 mins drive

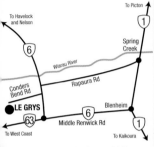

On SH 6 from Blenheim to Nelson,
Renwick is approx 8 minutes from
Blenheim. From Renwick, drive 2km
and turn left into Condors Bend Rd.
Le Grys is the third drive on the left.

Le Grys Vineyard Cottage and Homestay

John and Jennifer Joslin
119 Conders Bend Road, Renwick, Marlborough
Tel: 03 5729490   Mob: 021313208
Fax: 03 5729491
stay@legrys.co.nz
www.lodgings.co.nz – keyword: legrys

Set in the heart of Marlborough grape lands, Le Grys vineyard cottage is submerged in vines that reach out on all four sides, almost as far as the eye can see. This purpose built homestay is themed on a vineyard workers cottage. Vines are within touching distance on three sides whilst driveway and olive tree lined stream separates the front from the vines continued march toward distant hills. Of mud, or earth brick construction, in keeping with a 'workers cottage' theme, roof trusses were sourced from the old Picton Railway Station – quite remarkable timbers, certainly adding character and flavour to this romantic retreat. This is indeed a place to savour the romance of the vines and to perhaps appreciate the care and attention that goes into the growing of grapes. Here, however briefly, one is sharing the land with the vines and those who tend them. Here, one can start to appreciate the soul of winemaking. Enough of romance. Practicalities beckon. Talk to the hosts John and Jennifer. Winemakers in their own right, they will arrange a visit to nearby wineries, to further educate and enjoy the grape. Heading home to this vine nestled cottage perhaps a stop for some local product? What better than a barbeque under the stars amongst the vines? This truly is a wine lovers romantic getaway.

Family dog on site
Guest pets by arrangement

Breakfast: Provided in hamper

Guest rooms:
Ambience:
Setting/location:

LOW   HIGH

Accommodation available (NZ$)	👤	👤👤	+👤	🛏	🛁
1 S/C cottage	$250	$250	$50	Q+2S	PR
1 Room	$150	$150		Q	PR

TV in cottage. "Welcome" nibbles platter and wine on arrival day.

Broomfield Garden Cottages and Homestay

Kaye and Gary Green
31 Inkerman St, Renwick
Tel: 03 5728162
kaye.gary@xtra.co.nz
www.lodgings.co.nz – keyword: broomfield

Property features
Feature garden with potager
Rammed earth construction
Guest pick-up available
Open fire in winter
Local features
Vineyards/wineries
Golf course
Trout fishing
Horse and wagon trips
Gardens/museum
Olive groves

Renwick - 2 mins walk
Blenheim - 12 mins drive

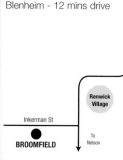

From Blenheim take Middle Renwick Rd to Renwick. Turn into Inkerman St on your right, Broomfield is 150m on your left.

This Beautiful home and two cottages are built over looking a spectacular garden, with the Marlborough Hills as a commanding backdrop. BEECHRON a two bedroom cottage at the bottom of Broomfield Garden is a 50 year old solid rimu building and has been lovingly restored and decorated in Scandinavian style using shades of soft blue, grey and white with a kingsize bed and fine linen. The attractive sitting/dining area includes a kitchenette. The newly restored WINTER cottage with one kingsize bedroom, ensuite, sitting/dining area is decorated in French country style has a log burner for colder days and a small adjourning kitchen. Within the house there is a large private guestroom upstairs. This has been decorated with the same flair as the cottages and overlooks the magnificent garden. Kaye and Gary are welcoming, helpful and considerate hosts. They take special pride in the sumptuous breakfasts they create for their guests. They are garden enthusiasts and their expertise is evident, with an abundance of colour, fragrance and creativity. In the traditional potager I eyed the ripening fruit on the espaliered vines, the vegetable bounty and sampled delicious berries. As I sat on the terrace at dusk enjoying a glass of wine, the rural setting, formal garden all conveyed a wonderful feeling of peace and relaxation.

Accommodation available (NZ$)	👤	👤👤	+👤	🛏	🛁	Guest pets by arrangement
1 Room	$150	$200		K	EN+PR	Breakfast: Special cooked
1 Cottage	$200	$220-240	$50	K+D	EN+PR	
1 Cottage	$200	$220-240		K	EN	Guest rooms:
						Ambience:
						Setting/location:

LOW   HIGH

Old Saint Mary's Convent Retreat

Layonie Seque
776 Rapaura Road, Blenheim
Tel: 03 5705700   Mob: 021488462
Fax: 03 5705703
retreat@convent.co.nz
www.lodgings.co.nz – keyword: saintmarys

Property features
Set on 60acres vineyard&parkland
Outdoor swimming pool
Petanque/croquet/bicycles
Full sized billards table
Restored church/guest library
Local features
Grass tennis courts - 1 min
Trout fishing - 10 mins
Wineries - 10 mins
Marlborough Sounds - 30 mins
Art galleries & cholcolate factory

Blenheim - 10 mins drive
Picton - 20 mins drive

From Christchurch take SH1 through Blenheim turning left into Rapaura Rd (H62) at Spring Creek Junction. Convent is approx 6 km on the Left. From Picton take H1 turning right into Rapaura Rd (SH62). Convent is approx 6km on the right.

This is a stunning building. What used to be the Saint Mary's Convent built in 1901 is now an up-market guest accommodation. This huge building, with its many verandahs, has five large suites for guests. The elegantly appointed living areas include a dining room and, because the Convent has recently been renovated, guests are provided with all modern luxuries in an environment that reflects the original use of the building. The honeymoon suite which is a replica of the original convent chapel, is beautifully, copied and furnished with such care, will take your breath away. The Convent is located on 60 acres of immaculately landscaped, formal lawn and gardens which are surrounded on all sides by vineyards and olive groves. My bedroom was spacious and light with a huge bathroom complete with a unique, deep, oval bath. All ensuites have claw-foot baths as well as showers and feature beautiful toiletries. Breakfast was fresh fruit, yoghurt and cereals and a full cooked selection, all elegantly served. There is an historic, deconsecrated church on the property that is mostly used for weddings and functions.

Family cats on site
Guest pets by arrangement

Breakfast: Cooked

Guest rooms:
Ambience:
Setting/location:

Accommodation available (NZ$)	👤	👥	+👤	🛏	🛁
1 Suite		$750	$80	SK + 2S	EN
1 Suite		$650	$80	K + 2S	EN
1 Room	$350	$550	$80	SK or T + 2S	EN
1 Room	$350	$550	$80	K + 2S	EN
1 Room	$350	$550	$80	Q	EN

123

St Leonards Vineyard Cottages

Daphne and Paul Radmall
18 St Leonards Road, Blenheim
Tel: 03 5778328   Mob: 0276861636
Fax: 03 5778329
stay@stleonards.co.nz
www.lodgings.co.nz – keyword: stleonards

Property features
Solar heated swimming pool
Lawn tennis court
Petanque court
Farm animals
Private & separate cottages
Local features
Wineries - 5 to 10 mins drive
Malborough Sounds - 30 mins drive
Whale watching - 90 mins drive
Farmers market - 5 mins drive
Water sports - 30 mins drive

Blenheim - 2 mins drive
Nelson - 90 mins drive

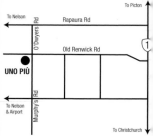

From Blenheim railway station take left at roundabout, (from Picton go right) onto Nelson St (beginning of S 6). Go through Blenheim towards th airport, 2km out is St Leonards Rd on right.

   Located on five acres of land in the heart of the Marlborough wine country, only a few kilometers from the town of Blenheim and surrounded by vineyards, are five charming cottages. Each cottage is as fabulous as the next. The Old Dairy is quaint and was once the dairy of the homestead, but now it has been redecorated into intimate and cosy accommodation. The original stables have also been renovated and would be a great choice for a romantic weekend as it is set well apart and has a fireplace to cuddle up in front of. As it was, I spent a delightful weekend in The Woolshed, the largest of the cottages, which has two bedrooms decorated with memorabilia from the old sheep-shearing days. The newest addition is simply called The Cottage and it has been designed to reflect the style of an old cob cottage. I enjoyed an early morning wander through the property among the fruit trees (I was encouraged to pick the fruit) and admiring the domesticated and friendly horses, sheep and chickens. Although there are five cottages they are positioned so that guests' privacy is assured.

Accommodation available (NZ$)	👤	👥	+👤	🛏	🛁	
1 S/C cottage	$180	$180		Q	EN	Breakfast: Continental
1 S/C cottage	$100	$100		Q	EN	
1 S/C cottage	$200	$200	$35	Q+S	PR	Guest rooms:
1 S/C house	$300	$300	$35	Q+3S	PR	Ambience:
1 S/C cottage	$145	$145	$35	Q+KS	EN	Setting/location:

Property features
Swimming pool/petanque
2 hectares gardens/paddocks
Sheep and horses on property
Baby grand piano
Italian hospitality
Guest lounge with open fire
Earth block cottage

Local features
Vineyards/wineries nearby
Golf courses/gardens
Trout fishing/walks

Blenheim - 5 mins drive
Airport - 5 mins drive

Uno Piu Homestead and Cottage

Gino and Heather Rocco
75 Murphy's Road, Blenheim
Tel: 03 5782235   Mob: 0211744257
Fax: 03 5782235
stay@unopiu.co.nz
www.lodgings.co.nz – keyword: unopiu

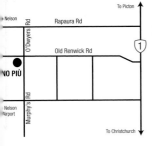

From Blenheim drive towards Nelson/Blenheim Airport on SH 6. Turn right into Murphys Rd. Uno Piu is 600m on the left.

Today's accepted translation of "boutique" conveys a sense of personalized style and exclusivity. Uno Piu, simply translated means "number one". It certainly is. Over the years we have experienced boutique accommodation at all levels. Some delight. Some disappoint. Uno Piu stuns. Set amongst delightful gardens, on a quiet road handy to town the house is graciously unpretentious. It isn't until welcomed inside one realizes that this is something special. One needs to pause to realize Gino and Heathers exquisite taste of décor and artwork. It is not in-your-face, demanding of attention but requires time to absorb such balance and harmony. It is everywhere one turns, be it furnishings, artwork or décor. Italian flavour in design and style is evident whilst attention to detail is superb. "Heather is the one" protests Gino "She has the eye for detail". And such detail! In the Guest rooms from bed to bath plug there is not one detail that is not of the best. There are no short cuts evident. There is nothing that has been done for expediency. And such a welcome! Hospitality in the refined European manner and the sharing of a glass of wine in the Kiwi way. How are such standards set? "We travel, we stay in lodges everywhere, we take the best and apply it here. It is our Passion". Stuns is not a word I've used before, but it's the only word that adequately describes our feelings for Uno Piu. Could I live here? Yes please.

Family pets on site
Guest pets by arrangement

Breakfast: Special 3 course
Evening meal: $80pp
Guest rooms:
Ambience:
Setting/location:

LOW   HIGH

Accommodation available (NZ$)	🧍	🧍🧍	+🧍	🛏	🛁
2 Rooms	$370	$430		K+SK or 2S	EN
1 S/C cottage		$470	$80	SK+Q+S	PR

Children in cottage only. Seasonal rates may apply.

Hapuku Lodge & Tree Houses

Rod and Belinda Ramsay
State Highway 1 - Station Road, RD1, Kaikoura
Tel: 03 3196559
Fax: 03 3196557
info@hapukulodge.com
www.lodgings.co.nz – keyword: hapuku

Property features
Spectacular mountain & sea views
Unique tree houses
Onsite Restaurant
Conference facilities
Local features
Kaikoura seaward mountain range
Mangamaunu Bay/hiking/biking
Marine safari/whale watching
Dolphins/deep see fishing
Night sky tours/scenic flights
Swimming/sea kayaking/winery tours

Kaikoura - 10 mins drive
Blenheim - 1 hr 45 mins drive

You will find Hapuku Lodge located
12kms (10mins) north of Kaikoura o
SH1. Go North across Hapuku Rive
Bridge, up a rise and you can't miss
the Lodge on the right hand side.

A stand out experience. Allow plenty of time. Just north of Kaikoura, on the coastal flat separating a restless ocean from towering snow topped mountain, there's a most extraordinary lodge set in a fully operational deer farm enhanced by olive groves, native plantings and well tended garden. There's a very strong feeling of place, of permanence. One imagines future generation sharing this delight. Married to the main lodge building and its more traditional guest suites are quirky Tree Houses. "They are a little different. You've just got to try one", responds the manager Rod. And we did. Perched amongst the treetops, unobtrusive columns firmly anchor each lofty eyrie. Access is by easily negotiated stairs. What delight awaits! Floor to ceiling glass frames magnificent mountains to the West whilst to the East, out over olive groves, there's Kaikoura's rugged coastline providing a gentle lullaby of rumbling surf. As in the lodge, the accent is on timeless longevity. Fixtures, fittings and furnishings are of the best whilst colour and décor reflect a "mountain to the sea" theme. The more blasé may say a room is just a room, not so the Tree House. I find it difficult to adequately describe the cocoon feeling the Tree House evokes, you've just got to try it. Could I stay here? Oh yes.....for ever.

Accommodation available (NZ$)	👤	👥	+👤	🛏	🛁		
3 Rooms	$310-390			Q	EN	Breakfast: Continental	
3 Rooms	$370-460			SK/T	EN	Evening meal: Restaurant	
5 Treehouses	$380-650			K/T	EN	Guest rooms:	
2 Treehouses	$690-850			2K/T	EN	Ambience:	
1 S/C Apt	$520-670	$75		K/T	EN	Setting/location:	

LOW   HIG

Property features
Outdoor bath
Lavender farm
Lavender shop on site
Display gardens
Local features
Whale watching
Seal colony
Swim with dolphins
Fishing
Golf course
Bush walks

Dylans Country Cottages

Mike and Maureen Morris
Postmans Road, Kaikoura
Tel 03 3195473
Fax 03 3195425
dylans.cs@clear.net.nz
www.lodgings.co.nz – keyword: dylans

Kaikoura - 10 mins drive
Blenheim - 1 hr 30 mins drive

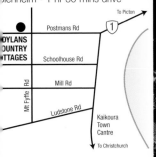

From SH 1 turn into Postmans
Rd, which is just north of Kaikoura
township. Continue past Mt Fyffe Rd
to Dylans on your right.

Nestled at the foot of Mt Fyffe, Dylans offers two rustic cottages, each with French doors, lots of exposed timber, a creative individual style and a large dose of country atmosphere. Both cottages are two storied, with queen beds upstairs and lounge/dining, kitchenette and bathroom downstairs. The Kowhai cottage has a funky bathroom with a spa bath, while the Mahoe cottage offers an outdoor bath and shower in addition to the usual bathroom facilities. Breakfast is a freshly made loaf of bread, homemade preserves and free range eggs. Dylans cottages are an integral part of a 5 acre working lavender farm and display gardens. There is also an onsite lavender shop with a wide range of products related to relaxation and well being. With all that Dylans has to offer it is guaranteed that your stay will be restful and provide a unique experience. These cottages are designed for your privacy but friendly hosts are only a few steps away. Kaikoura township is only a short 10 minute drive away where I found numerous local shops, cafes and restaurants. Whale watching tours are famous at this quaint seaside town.

Family pets on site

Accommodation available (NZ$)	♦	♦♦	+♦	🛏	🛁
1 S/C unit	$150	$150	$15	Q+S	PR
1 S/C unit	$150	$150	$15	Q+S	PR

Breakfast: Continental

Guest rooms:
Ambience:
Setting/location:

LOW   HIGH

Both units also have fold out double divan beds. Enquire for children's tariffs.

Fyffe Country Lodge

Chris Rye and Colin Ashworth
458 State Highway 1, Kaikoura
Tel: 03 3196869
Fax: 03 3196865
fyffe@xtra.co.nz
www.lodgings.co.nz – keyword: fyffe

Property features
Licensed award wining restaruant
Individually decored rooms
Lounge bar
Wedding venue
English gardens
Local features
Whalewatching
Dolphine swimming
Golf/horse riding
Helicopter & plane flights
Seal swimming

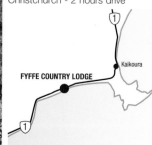

Blenheim - 1 1/2 hrs drive
Christchurch - 2 hours drive

The lodge is situated 6km south of Kaikoura township along State Highway 1. Advanced warning signage appears 300 metres from property entrance.

Built of rammed earth with a steep pitched cedar shingle roof, one imagines the time when such lodges served horse-drawn coach and carriage. Although built as recently as 1992, with all modern amenities, the feeling of yesteryear is enhanced by 100 year old doors and windows salvaged from the districts early history. Owners Chris and Colin do almost everything, from glorious gardens to gourmet restaurant. "It's our delight to bring our personal touch to the guest experience. In fact we never allow the property to be run under management for that very reason." As for that personal touch, Fyffe Country Lodge is a paradise for the ladies. Chris has exquisite taste reflected everywhere one turns, but especially in bed linens. There's a range of accommodation, from well sized (and exquisitely decored) rooms to a truly magnificent suite, which, in itself would be considered a spacious apartment in London or Paris. All whale watched out? Seen enough seals? Stop and buy a cooked crayfish from one of the many roadside stalls. With Colin or Chris' help, select a suitable local wine to complement it, then take a table in their sunny sheltered brick courtyard. Might need a siesta after such indulgence, then dine in or tackle Kaikoura night life. Next mornings breakfast is a leisurely affair the free range eggs coming from hens observed scratching around the garden fringe. Oh, those beds, dressed to perfection!

Accommodation available (NZ$)	👤	👥	+👤	🛏	🛁	
4 Rooms	$180	$320	$75	K	EN	Breakfast: Cooked
1 Room	$275	$395	$75	K	EN	
1 Room	$350	$600	$100	K	EN	Guest rooms:
						Ambience:

Evening meal available at the on site licenced award wining restaruant.

Setting/location:

LOW   HIG

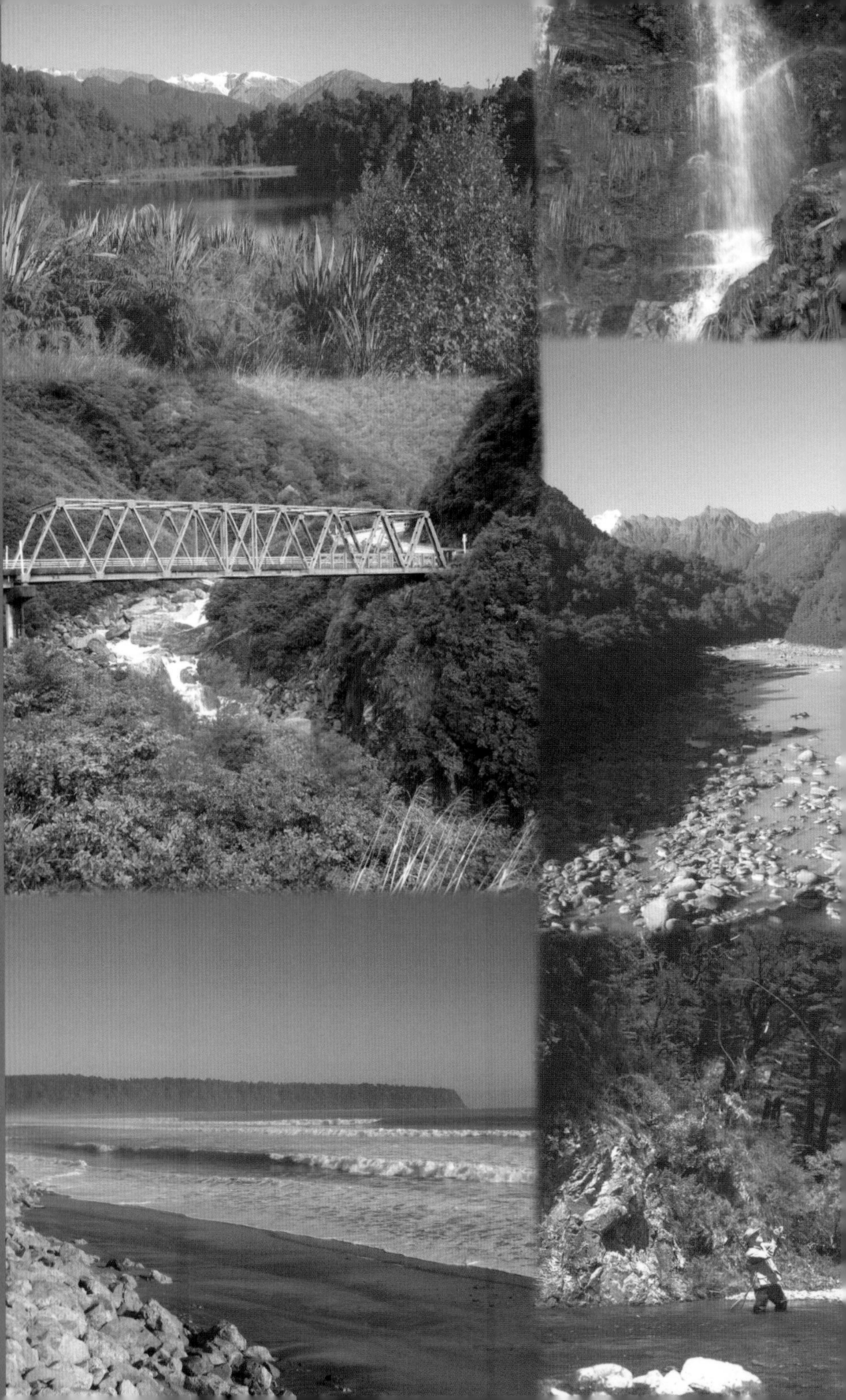

Courtesy of Rough and Tumble Bush Lodge

Rough and Tumble Bush Lodge

Susan Cook, Marion 'Weasel' Boatwright
Mokihinui Road, Seddonville, Westport
Tel: 03 7821337
Fax: 03 7821333
godeep@roughandtumble.co.nz
www.lodgings.co.nz – keyword: roughtumble

qualmark
★ ★ ★ ★ plus
guest 6 hosted

Property features
Trout fishing/walking/kayaking
Romantic bush bath for two
Large sundrenched decks
Open fire/library/board games
Guided glow worm walks
Local features
Heaphy Track - 50 mins
Charming Creek Walkway - 15 min
Mt Glasgow Route - 12 mins
Mokihinui Track - 20 mins
Chasm Creek Walkway - 6 mins

Ⓟ 🚶 ✉ 📺 ☏ ♿   💳 MasterCard VISA eftpos Diners Club

Westport - 40 mins drive
Karamea - 45 mins drive

ROUGH AND
TUMBLE BUS
LODGE

Westport
6

From SH 67 north of Westport, rig
to Seddonville, straight through tov
- past last farmhouse. Gravel road
1.7km until the ford follow signs to
lodge 800m.

Leave Westport behind and travel north. This not so well known coastal highway is spectacular. Head through Seddonville and you just might suspect that you are indeed going to nowhere, Turn into the long driveway and it just keeps getting better. Over the ford and up to the lodge perched on the riverbank and the vista takes your breath away. This is no ordinary stream this is the mighty Mokihinui in all its glory. Summer, winter it's a different picture by the hour. Marion (Weasel) and Sue have literally hand crafted this spectacular lodge from scratch. Tables fashioned from wood, fireplaces from stones from the river bed, right down to the door handles and picture frames. This is a work of love and art. I was shown to my room and the view back towards the mountains as the sun went down was as impressive as the river. I joined Sue and Marion for drinks and a beautiful three course dinner and we chatted like long lost friends. There are just so many activities, bush walks, swim the rivers and the fishing on the door step is legendary, kayak or for that very special romantic touch the outdoor bath riverside, champagne in hand. There is no cell phone or internet coverage thank goodness. Well what else can you say, if this is "roughing and tumbling" it – bring it on!

Accommodation available (NZ$)	🧍	🧍🧍	+🧍	🛏	🛁	Guest pets not welcome
5 Rooms	$250	$400	$155	K+K or 2S	EN	

Sumptuous three course dinner and breakfast included in the tariff.
BYO License.

Breakfast: Special cooked
Evening meal: Included
Guest rooms:
Ambience:
Setting/location:

RECOMMENDED
★★★★★
BOUTIQUE
LODGINGS
LOW   HI

Property features
Spa
Dinners and house bar
33 acres with many walks
Personalised local tour service
Local features
Paparoa National Park
Seal colony at Tauranga Bay
Historic Denniston & Charleston
Gold mining
Glow worm walks/caves
Horse riding/jet boat/kayaking

Bird's Ferry Lodge - Ferry Man's Cottage

Alison and Andre Gygax
Bird's Ferry Road, Westport, West Coast
Mob: 021337217
Free: 0800212207
info@birdsferrylodge.co.nz
www.lodgings.co.nz – keyword: birdsferry

Westport - 15 mins drive
Charleston - 8 mins drive

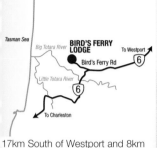

17km South of Westport and 8km north of Charleston on SH6. Watch for our sign on the highway, then follow private gravel road for 2km.

Perched on the edge of a glacial terrace and overlooking a wide valley covered with native rain forest you will find Bird's Ferry Lodge located midway between the glaciers and Nelson/Picton. Alison, who hails from Scotland, and Andre, originally from Cape Town, and Mick and Merlot the two charming terriers are there to greet me. Alison has spent 15 years in the catering business and both she and Andre are keen gardeners so naturally the kitchen is a centre of activity with most of the produce and free-range eggs being turned into culinary delights. The lodge has three well appointed bedrooms. A recent addition, the Ferry Man's Cottage, overlooks a lake so your fellow residents are native wekas, pukeko's and ducks. Quirky artworks fashioned from pieces of history or interesting flora abound. The West Coast is steeped in history and Andre, who spent many years as a guide, is a wealth of knowledge and can fill you in on all the details including the story of Mr Bird's ferry after whom the lodge is named. Relax with a glass of champagne in the spa or the outdoor bath and enjoy the peace and serenity. Surrounded by birdsong and the constant rumble of the Tasman Sea you won't need any entertainment here, the changing scenery will do it for you. One day is just not long enough here.

Family dog on site
Guest pets by arrangement

	Accommodation available (NZ$)	👤	👥	+👤	🛏	🛁
Breakfast: Cooked	2 Rooms	$200-250			Q	EN
Evening meal: $65pp	1 Room	$200-250			D	EN
Guest rooms:	1 S/C cottage	$200-300	$30	Q/SK/T		EN
Ambience:	Three course evening meals available from 7pm approximately.					
Setting/location:	Includes NZ wine. Dinner requires prior notification. Wireless internet available.					

Breakers

Jan Macdonald
9 Mile Creek, SH6, Coast Road, Greymouth
Tel: 03 7627743
Fax: 03 7627733   Free: 0800350590
stay@breakers.co.nz
www.lodgings.co.nz – keyword: breakers

Property features
Tasman Sea Views from all rooms
Mountain views/2 acre gardens
Private beach access
West coast sunsets
TV/tea/coffee facilites in all rooms
Local features
Paparoa National Park
Hiking/biking/caving/rafting
Arthurs Pass/National Park
Jade carving/wood turning
Glass blowing

Greymouth - 10 mins drive
Punakaki - 20 mins drive

Breakers is located on the Coast
Road, (State Highway 6) at Nine Mil
Creek, 14kms north from Greymout

   The name says it all because from every room in the house I could hear the waves of the Tasman Sea crashing below. This New Zealand style accommodation is set above one of the West Coast's amazing beaches. Breakers has four guestrooms, two of which are in the house. Both have sea views, queen-size beds and access to a large balcony. The other two rooms are away from the main house in a separate wing and have views over Mussel Point. These two rooms are more modern but still in keeping with the New Zealand 'bach' (small seaside cottage) theme. I stayed in one of the newer rooms called the Sunset Room, which had a large king-size bed where I lay in the morning with the curtains and door open to enjoy the sea view while I had a cup of tea in bed. The house is surrounded by piles of driftwood and river rocks which have been collected from local beaches. Jan prepared a lovely breakfast and gave me advice about the sort of activities I might enjoy during the day. She loves the outdoors and had many walks to recommend.

Accommodation available (NZ$)	🧍	🧍🧍	+🧍	🛏	🛁	Family dog on site Guest pets by arrangement
1 Room		$190-195		Q	EN	Breakfast: Cooked
1 Room		$255-285	$50	Q+S	EN	Evening meal: $70pp
1 Suite		$285-325	$50	K+S	EN	Guest rooms:
1 Suite		$285-325		K	EN	Ambience:

Peace and tranquility - great place to relax and unwind.

Setting/location:

LOW   HIG

Property features
Outdoor seating
Garden
Wireless internet
Sky TV
Local features
Museum
Art gallery
Brewery tour
Jade gallery
Bush walks

Rosewood Bed and Breakfast
Rhonda and Stephan Palten
20 High Street, Greymouth
Tel: 03 7684674   Mob: 0272427080
Fax: 03 7684694   Free: 0800185748
stay@rosewoodnz.co.nz
www.lodgings.co.nz – keyword: rosewood

(P) 🚶 ✉ 📺 ℂ ♿

MasterCard VISA eftpos

Greymouth - 15 mins walk
Hokitika - 30 mins drive

Rosewood is located on SH6, 1.4km
south of the town centre.

Rosewood Bed and Breakfast is conveniently situated close to the center of Greymouth. On entering the gates to the pretty garden I was greeted by Rhonda and Stephan. Stepping through the door is a step back into historic New Zealand. Built around the 1920's, wood paneling, leadlight windows and native timbers abound, all beautifully restored. That is not to say there is a shortage of modern luxuries and comforts one has come to expect. We sat at the large Rimu table and chattered over a drink and homemade baking while enjoying the warmth of the fireplace. Breakfast consisting of fruit, home made muesli, preserves was also served here. Stephan, a chef is happy to cook to your individual requirements and his omelettes' are legendary. His artistic ability also extends to the gardens and guest areas were he has added personal touches utilizing such things as driftwood from the nearby beach. The guest rooms all tastefully furnished and spacious had all the comforts to make my stay relaxing. Rhonda and Stephan both speak fluent German and are happy to assist with any travel arrangements or advise on the numerous scenic unspoiled walkways, rivers and beaches nearby. Rosewood Bed and Breakfast is the perfect place to chill out and feel at home while planning visits to the Glaciers or the pancake rocks at Punakaiki.

Guest pets by arrangement	Accommodation available (NZ$)	👤	👥	+👤	🛏	🛁
Breakfast: Cooked	2 Rooms	$180	$220		Q	EN
	1 Room		$200	$50	Q + 1S	PR
Guest rooms:	1 Room	$190	$235	$50	K or 2S	EN
Ambience:						
Setting/location:						

LOW   HIGH

135

Lake Brunner Lodge

The Team
Mitchells, RD 1, Kumara
Tel: 03 7380163
Fax: 03 730173
lodge@lakebrunner.co.nz
www.lodgings.co.nz – keyword: lakebrunner

Property features
Hydro power system
Organic vegetable garden
Lake frontage
Water features
Local features
Carew Waterfall/bush walk - 25 mins
Bains Bay track - 1 hour
Farm tours by arrangememt
Native glow worm dell - 10 mins
Numerous lake activites

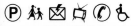

Greymouth - 50 mins drive
Hokitika - 50 mins drive

From Greymouth, head south on SH 6, From Hokitika head north to the Kumara Junction to Arthurs Pass 7km, left at sign to Mitchells 9kms,le over bridge. 12km (gravel Rd) until you view the lake. Lodge on right.

Situated close to the very heart of Westland is Lake Brunner. Driving the 22km to Lake Brunner Lodge from the famed junction of Kumara you know that you are in for an experience. The gravel road winds through beautiful West Coast rainforest with the canopy of trees filled with bird life. Suddenly it's there, Lake Brunner with the lodge nestled in the trees on the right. The welcome sign is out. This renowned historic property with its 1930's architecture has undergone a metamorphosis and every possible luxury is there for guests. The rooms are beautifully appointed, decorated with modern, relaxing furnishings all offset with native timbers. We head to the lounge and library, and enjoy a pre dinner drink and swap stories with our fellow travellers before a sumptuous dinner. The menu changes daily, utilising the very best of local ingredients, venison, lamb, seafood and organic produce from the lodge gardens. What to do was the next dilemma: farm tour, mountain biking, kayaking, fishing, the lake spread out before us won. Tomorrow is another day. We settled in for several days, the wonderful staff ensured we wanted for nothing. Lake Brunner Lodge is totally self sustainable with its own power system, and land regeneration scheme and is an excellent example of New Zealand's Eco-Tourism programme. If we thought getting to Lake Brunner Lodge was a challenge, leaving was much harder, why would you want to.

Accommodation available (NZ$)	👤	👥	+👤	🛏	🛁	
3 Rooms	$313-470	$275-390	$180	K	EN	Breakfast: Special Cooked
2 Rooms	$286-390	$260-315	$180	Q	EN	
1 Room	$286-390	$260 315	$180	Q + S	EN	Guest rooms:
1 Room	$286-390	$260-315	$180	K	EN	Ambience:
4 course Dinner is included in the tariff.						Setting/location:

LOW   HIGI

Property features
Incl. Breakfast & 4-course dinner
Incl. 2 guided farm/nature activities
6180 acre range/forest/river/lakes
DOC Licence CA 15048
Working sheep station/guided walks
Sheep shearing/kayaking
Local features
Beech forest & alpine tracks
Arthur's Pass National Park
Wild rivers and high country lakes
Fishing - trout and salmon

Arthur's Pass - 15 mins drive
Christchurch - 2 hours drive

The Lodge is 16km east of Arthur's
Pass township on Highway 73.
Transfers from train station can be
arranged. Shuttle bus stops at lodge.

Wilderness Lodge Arthur's Pass
Deb Skelton and Wally Bruce
State Highway 73, Arthur's Pass
Tel: 03 3189246
Fax: 03 3189245
arthurspass@wildernesslodge.co.nz
www.lodgings.co.nz – keyword: wildnessap

Nestled in a mountain beech forest clearing in the heart of the Southern Alps, this 24-four room lodge is surrounded by Arthur's Pass National Park. Each of the spacious guestrooms have superb views and feature New Zealand timbers. Recent additions to the lodge are the four Alpine Lodges, which are separated from the main lodge and have been stylishly furnished with a super-king-size bed, a lounge and balcony that looks out to landscaped gardens and the mountains. This is a high quality, professionally run operation. Maps help guests to explore the 20 kilometres of easy walking tracks on their own, or they can join in the Lodges guided nature adventure programme. Included in the tariff is a daily program of shorter, guided, nature and farm tours including mustering and sheep shearing, canoeing on high country lakes and exploring beech forest and tussock lands to look for birds and alpine plants. I was amazed at how much there was to learn about the environment, even in the immediate area around the lodge. This lodge is associated with Wilderness Lodge Lake Moeraki in the rainforests of South Westland. Both are designed to show that well managed ecotourism can both protect the environment and provide employment to small communities.

Guest pets by arrangement	Accommodation available (NZ$)	👤	👥	+👤	🛏	🛁
Breakfast: Cooked	20 Rooms	$330-430	$460-660		Q+S	EN
Evening Meal: Included	4 Lodges	$590-690	$780-980		SK/T	EN
Guest rooms:						
Ambience:						
Setting/location:		Tariff incl. 4 course dinner, breakfast, 2 guided short nature activities daily.				

Awatuna Homestead

Pauline and Hemi Te Rakau
9 Stafford Road, Awatuna, RD2, Hokitika 7882
Tel: 03 7556834
Fax: 03 7556876
rest@awatunahomestead.co.nz
www.lodgings.co.nz – keyword: awatuna

Property features
2.5 acres of native garden
Outside spa in bush setting
Vintage cars on site
Eco friendly
Peaceful private setting
Local features
Helicopter flights from homestead
3 National Parks/beach
Fishing guides arranged
Jade, glass, gold crafts

Hokitika - 10 mins drive
Greymouth - 20 mins drive

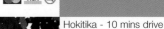

From SH 6 just south of Kumara Junction, turn into Stafford Rd at Awatuna (approx. 25 km south of Greymouth, 12km north of Hokitika). Cross railway line, Awatuna Homestead is first on the left.

This coastal retreat set beside the tranquil Waimea River has a peaceful and relaxing environment. Pauline, Hemi and family have lived here for over 30 years and combine the warmth of a family atmosphere with the luxury of a boutique lodging. The homestead is set among plantings of native trees and shrubs which foster bird-life. Nature and culture come together because many of the plant varieties are steeped in Maori tradition. It's a special experience to relax in the spa pool that is set among native trees and listen to the roaring of the sea, a five-minute walk away. Hemi, a retired cultural advisor to the Department of Conservation, speaks Maori and is willing to share his knowledge of the Pacific navigators, language, customs and traditional stories of his people during the evening. The ambience of the homestead is complemented by an open fire in the guest lounge, a room in which guests relax in the evening after a full day and a meal of country cuisine for which Pauline is renowned. There is so much adventure and excitement in this region and this is a good place to base yourself while you explore the options, as Awatuna is situated between Greymouth and Hokitika.

Accommodation available (NZ$)	👤	👥	+👤	🛏	🛁	Family pets on site
1 Room	$230	$250		2S	EN	Breakfast: Cooked
1 Room		$290		1Q	EN	Evening meal: $65pp
1 Room		$350		SK or 2S	EN/Spa	Guest rooms:
1 S/C unit		$240	$35	Q,D,2S	PR	Ambience:
S/C unit: breakfast is $20pp extra.						Setting/location:

Property features
Icon heritage building
Quiet, central location
Separate guest lounge
Internet facilities
Local features
Museum & Info centre - 1 min walk
Beach - 5 min walk
Golf course - 8 min drive
Airport - 8 min drive
Lake Kaniere - 20 min drive
Hokitika Gorge - 40 min drive

Teichelmann's Bed and Breakfast

Frances Flanagan & Brian Ward
20 Hamilton Street, Hokitika
Tel: 03 7558232   Mob: 0272558232
Fax: 03 7558239
teichel@xtra.co.nz
www.lodgings.co.nz – keyword: teichelmann

 10

Hokitika - 1 min walk
Greymouth - 40 mins drive

Turn left at Hokitika town clock
then first right into Hamilton Street.
Teichelmann's Bed and Breakfast
is on the right hand side across
the road from the Museum and
information centre.

Situated in the heart of Hokitika, Teichelmann's is a part of West Coast history. Dr Ebenezer Teichelmann was a renowned surgeon, mountaineer, photographer and conservationist. This historic home and medical rooms has been meticulously preserved with many wonderful examples of memorabilia from the era. Frances and Brian are the perfect kiwi hosts. The five double bedrooms are all tastefully decorated with beautiful linens, ensuite bathrooms and many personal touches. Alternatively choose Teichy's garden cottage. Relax in this wonderful garden studio unit, enjoy the spa bath overlooking the miners' cottage garden. Teichelmann's is perfectly situated for exploring the national park areas of the beautiful West Coast. Many of the well renowned art and craft centres are within walking distance. Frances and Brian are only too happy to help with travel plans, arranging dinner bookings at adjacent restaurants or you may choose to relax and enjoy the surroundings. Breakfast is served in the dining room and is not to be missed. Enjoy a choice of cereals, fruits, delicious home made breads, and your choice of cooked breakfast, all beautifully presented. There is a time when one needs to feel pampered and spoilt and Teichelmann's is the perfect place while absorbing a part of history.

Accommodation available (NZ$)	🧍	🧍🧍	+🧍	🛏	🛁
2 Rooms	$175	$195		K	EN
1 Room	$175	$210	$40	K + KS	PR
1 Room	$175	$210		K	EN
1 Room	$165			D	EN
1 Cottage	$185	$240		K	EN

Breakfast: Cooked

Guest rooms:
Ambience:
Setting/location:

Rimu Lodge

Helen and Peter Walls
33 Seddons Terrace Road, Rimu, Hokitika
Tel: 03 7555255   Mob: 0276487060
Fax: 03 7555237
rimulodge@xtra.co.nz
www.lodgings.co.nz – keyword: rimulodge

  14

Property features
Large stone open fireplace
Large outside deck
Spectacular river and bush views
Local features
Golf course nearby
Trout fishing tours
Glaciers/ Mt Cook
Milford Sound flights
Punakaiki - pancake rocks

Hokitika - 10 mins drive
Greymouth - 40 mins drive

From Hokitika, travel south across Hokitika Bridge, turn first left into Arthurstown Rd. Travel 4km to intersection, turn right into Woodstock-Rimu Rd. At Rimu, turn left into Seddons Terrace Rd. Rimu Lodge is 300 metres on left.

Rimu lodge is elegant and intimate and overlooks the Hokitika River and distant alpine peaks. The building has a steeply pitched roof which fits in with the mountainous surroundings and the views from the property are unparalleled. It was once a family holiday home but hosts, Helen and Peter, felt it was too good to keep to themselves. The guest lounge has cathedral-like ceilings and I enjoyed sitting in this space, in front of a roaring fire, before evening drinks were served. There are four guestrooms, each with spacious ensuites. They are decorated with modern, good taste and have plenty of room to spread out in. I woke up in the morning and through my window was a surreal view of the mountain peaks rising majestically out of the mist. Breakfast was served on the deck where Helen offered me wonderful home-made muesli and the option of a cooked breakfast. She recounted interesting stories about the area and gave me advice on what to do during my stay. Rimu Lodge is well-placed if guests want to explore the region, but it is also a treat to relax and enjoy the lodge.

Accommodation available (NZ$)	🧍	🧍🧍	+🧍	🛏	🛁	Family dog on site
1 Room	$235	$255		Q	EN	Breakfast: Special cooked
1 Room	$235	$295		Q	EN	
1 Room	$235	$325		K	EN	Guest rooms:
1 Room	$235	$325		SK/T	EN	Ambience:
						Setting/location:

LOW   HIGH

Property features
Award winning gardens
Rocky Mountain Elk farm tour
Glow-worm tour
Large spacious rooms
Dinner available
Local features
Forest walk - 10 mins
Craft Shop - 10 mins
Aircraft museum and park - 5 mins
Brown trout fly fishing - 5 mins
Glaciers - 45 mins

Hari Hari - 10 mins walk
Hokitika - 45 mins drive

Located one hour south of Hokitika, take SH6 to Harihari. Wapiti Park Homestead is just south of Harihari, on the west side of the highway.

Wapiti Park Homestead
Grant and Beverleigh Muir
State Highway 6, Hari Hari, South Westland, West Coast
Tel: 03 7533074   Mob: 021385252
Fax: 03 7533024   Free: 0800927484
wapitipark@xtra.co.nz
www.lodgings.co.nz – keyword: wapitipark

Wapiti Park Homestead is the perfect place for exploring the South Island's dramatic West Coast. This wonderful homestead is surrounded by beautiful gardens on a 50 acre farm specializing in breeding Wapiti (Rocky Mountain Elk). Grant and Beverleigh, the owner hosts are very knowledgeable about the local flora, fauna and history. Their homestead is a large two storey building with three very spacious suites with ensuite's all luxuriously appointed and ensuring maximum privacy. Relaxing in the lounges, curling up by the enormous fire, the library or games room, there were so many options for me to choose, and that was before I ventured outside. I started the day with the farm tour feeding the Wapiti, and then tried a little fly fishing in the world renowned La Fontaine stream. For trophy hunters there is the possibility of Himalayan Thar or Chamois on one of Grant's hunting safaris. Alternatives were scenic flights, numerous rainforest walks and treks, visit the white heron sanctuary, the after dinner glow-worm experience and much more. After a wonderful day exploring I joined my hosts for pre- dinner drinks before a truly memorable dinner featuring local produce and South Island wines. Had I been more skilled at fly fishing, my hosts would have been happy to prepare my catch. There is just so much to see and do, it is essential that you put time aside to experience all that is Wapiti Park Homestead.

Family cat on site

Accommodation available (NZ$)	🧍	🧍🧍	+🧍	🛏	🛁
1 Suite	$300	$375	$95	K+1S	EN
2 Suites	$436	$545		SK or T	EN

Breakfast: Special cooked
Evening meal: $75pp
Guest rooms:
Ambience:
Setting/location:

LOW   HIGH

Single party "exclusive use" available, POA. Maximum of 6 persons.

Franz Josef Glacier Country Retreat

Marie and Glenn Coburn
State Highway 6, Lake Mapourika, Franz Josef Glacier
Tel: 03 7520012   Mob: 0275451198
Fax: 03 7520021   Free: 0800372695
stay@glacier-retreat.co.nz
www.lodgings.co.nz - keyword: franzjosefretreat

Property features
Restaurant & bar on site
4th generation local host
Guest lounge open fire
Peaseful country setting
Mountain & lake views
Local features
Glacier scenic flights
Guided glacier hikes
Fishing
Rainforest walks / bird watching
Horse trekking & kayaking

Franz Josef - 5 mins drive
Hokitika - 90 mins drive

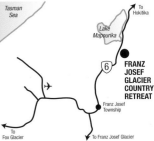

From Hokitika travel south on SH6 for 1 1/2 hours. The retreat is located 2 km south of Lake Mapourika. Turn left into the first large entrance signposted. From Franz Josef the retreat is 6km north on SH6. Turn right into the first large entrance signposted.

Turning off the highway and driving through the farmland to Franz Josef Glacier Country Retreat sitting on a crest, the homestead looks as if it has been there since time began. The hosts Marie and Glenn and their daughter Sophia- Rose are genuine Westcoasters' and Franz Josef Glacier Country Retreat is the result of a total family commitment. The impressive homestead is a replica of an original homestead and the 200 acres of land has been in the family for a number of generations. The twelve beautifully appointed guest suites are all named after local identities and colours have been carefully chosen to reflect their individual personalities. This is the perfect place to share that romantic occasion with a loved one or indulge in a passion for fishing. I wandered down to the river a few meters away on Glenn's advice as it was time for the spawning of the salmon, and while I did not spot one, what a perfect spot to relax and view the magnificent scenery. Marie and Glenn are very knowledgeable on the history of the area and are very happy to assist with holiday plans, however you may choose to join a cheese making class, a pamper weekend or numerous other activities that may be on at the time. Spending a few days with this wonderful family soon had me feeling like I was a true "Westcoaster".

Accommodation available (NZ$)	👤	👤👤	+👤	🛏	🛁	Family cat on site Guest pets by arrangement
4 Rooms	$225-325	$225-325	Q	EN		Breakfast: Cooked
6 Rooms	$225-325	$225-325	K	EN		Evening Meal: $35-75pp
1 Room	$325-425	$325-425	K	PR		Guest rooms:
1 Room	$425-525	$425-525	Q	PR		Ambience:
Iron and laundry facilities available.						Setting/location:

LOW   HIGH

Property features
Apartment style complex
1 or 2 bedroom options
Quiet country setting
Mountain and native bush views
Childrens playground
Local features
Guided glacier walks / heli hikes
Scenic flights
Guided quad bike tours
Kayaking and glacial hike tours
World famous glaciers

Glenfern Villas

Wendy and Marcel Fekkes
State Highway 6, Franz Josef Glacier, West Coast
Tel: 03 7520054   Mob: 0275499686
Fax: 03 7520174   Free: 0800453633
host@glenfern.co.nz
www.lodgings.co.nz - keyword: glenfern

Franz Josef - 5 mins drive
Fox Glacier - 30 mins drive

From Franz Josef Glacier township head north on State Highway 6 for three kilometres. Glenfern Villas is on your right.

Planning an escape to the West Coast, then the Glenfern Villas situated just outside Franz Josef village is the perfect place from which to explore the tranquility and beauty of the Westland National Park. Whether traveling as a couple, a family or with a group of friends the Glenfern Villas offer luxurious one or two bedroom villas to suit the most discerning traveler. Our party found the Villas, all of which are luxuriously appointed with fully equipped kitchens the ideal place to base ourselves. Some of us took the time to unwind and enjoy the natural beauty of the wild West Coast, while the rest took the opportunity to indulge in the more energetic activities, including Heli Hiking over the world famous Franz Josef Glacier. Other options include guided walks, jet boating, hunting or fishing. There is so much to see and do in this area that our decision to stop for a few days proved to be very rewarding. Our hosts at Glenfern Villas were very knowledgeable and a great help assisting with our planning. At the end of a day exploring we had the choice of self catering, relaxing with a drink outdoors watching the sun go down and star gazing or heading into the village to the numerous cafes and bars to experience the West Coast hospitality. Glenfern Villas, the perfect home away from home.

Family pets on site

Accommodation available (NZ$)	♦	♦♦	+♦	⬒	🛁
Breakfast: Continental	8 S/C apartments $195	$195	$30	Q	PR
	2 S/C apartments $195	$195	$30	K or T	PR
Guest rooms:	4 S/C Villas $245	$245	$30	2Q	PR
Ambience:	4 S/C Villas $245	$245	$30	Q + 3S	PR
Setting/location:	Apartments are 1 bedroom. Villas are 2 bedroom. Tariff for extra child is $15.				

Tariff for extra child is $15.

Holly Homestead Bed & Breakfast

Gerard and Bernie Oudemans
State Highway 6, Franz Josef Glacier
Tel: 03 7520299
Fax: 03 7520298
stay@hollyhomestead.co.nz
www.lodgings.co.nz – keyword: hollyhomestead

Property features
Central heating and log fire
Friendly NZ born hosts
Rural and mountain views
Relaxed atmosphere
Warm timber theme
Local features
Guided Glacier walks/heli hikes
Scenic flights
Bush/lakes and coastal walks
Horse trekking and kayaking
White Heron sanctuary tour

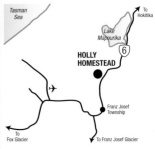

Franz Josef - 2 mins drive
Hokitika - 90 mins drive

On SH6, 1.5km north of Franz Josef Glacier township.

This historic 1920's house is one of Franz Josef Glacier's oldest wooden homesteads and is built from the native timbers in the Arts and Crafts style. The hosts, Gerard and Bernie, have spent the last few years restoring the homestead and making it the warm and inviting place it is today. When I arrived, a comforting fire was burning in the fireplace in the main living room. I was invited to join Gerard and Bernie for a cup of tea and homemade muffins and they took the time to find out what I had planned for my stay and to provide me with tips of what I must see while I was there. The homestead has four ensuite guestrooms and one suite, all superbly appointed with old-world charm. The homestead is perfectly positioned for the outdoor activity the area is known for – hiking, guided glacier walks, scenic flights and kayaking, to name a few. I took time out in the afternoon for a scenic flight over the glaciers, which was a fantastic adventure. Breakfast is served at the large dining table just off the kitchen which overlooks the alpine views. Guests are seated with each other providing a great chance to meet other travellers and exchange travel tips while enjoying Gerard's cooking.

Accommodation available (NZ$)	👤	👤👤	+👤	🛏	🛁	
2 Rooms	$170-230	$200-260		Q	EN	Breakfast: Cooked
2 Rooms	$200-260	$230-290		SK or 2S	EN	
1 Suite	$300-400	$300-400		SK	EN	Guest rooms:
						Ambience:
						Setting/location:

Enquire about minimum stay nights and winter discounts. Internet and phone available.

LOW   HIGH

Property features
Set in a beautiful bush garden
Views of rainforest and mountains
Superb open plan super king suites
Stylish ensuite bathrooms
Lounge/bar with impressive fire
Withdraw to the billiard room
Local features
Senic flights/Heli-Hikes
Eco-tours & range of water sports
Buzzing with adventure activity
Situated in Westland National Park

Westwood Lodge
Richard Jones and Jacquie Green
State Highway 6, Franz Josef, Westland
Tel: 03 7520112
Fax: 03 7520111
info@westwoodlodge.co.nz
www.lodgings.co.nz – keyword: westwoodlodge

Franz Josef - 2 mins drive
Greymouth - 2 hours drive

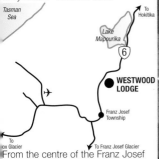

From the centre of the Franz Josef
village travel 1km north along SH
6. Or you can take a pleasant walk
for 15mins along the designated
footpath. The lodge is on your right.

The drive to the West Coast is dramatic, and turning into the welcoming lights of Westwood Lodge was a satisfying end to the day. It wasn't long before we were relaxing in the lounge in front of the impressive fireplace with our hosts Jacquie and Richard enjoying a welcoming drink. We swapped stories about our day and were then shown our room. Westwood Lodge has three suites in the main house and there are six coach house suites. The warmth of natural timber throughout reflects the New Zealand West Coast forest environment and the contemporary furnishings are complemented by artworks from inspired New Zealand artist, Melanie Hammett. The main house suites all feature stunning relaxing French tubs. We eyed this up for later, made sure the champagne was on hand and headed into the village a mere three minutes drive away to a restaurant that Jacquie and Richard had recommended. The morning dawned to reveal the native gardens melding into the most spectacular views of the mountains and glacier. Following a superb breakfast a glacier visit was in order, alternatively we could have made a visit to Hukawai, the indoor ice climbing wall to test our skills or we could have relaxed with a book from the library or played pool. Westwood Lodge, perfect for the romantic holiday can also cater for that special breakaway for business teams. Nothing was a problem.

Accommodation available (NZ$)	👤	👥	+👤	🛏	🛁
6 Suites	$320	$320	$160	K/T	EN
2 Suites	$320	$320		K	EN
1 Suite	$370	$370		K	EN

Breakfast: Cooked

Guest rooms:
Ambience:
Setting/location:

Fax, laundry, safe, mail posting and library facilities available. Voltage adaptors are also available.

Wilderness Lodge Lake Moeraki

Anne Saunders and Gerry McSweeney
State Highway 6, Lake Moeraki, South Westland
Tel: 03 7500881
Fax: 03 7500882
lakemoeraki@wildernesslodge.co.nz
www.lodgings.co.nz – keyword: wildernesslm

Property features
Incl. 4-course evening meal
Incl. shorter guided nature options
Trout fishing gear for hire
Canoe safaris/kayaks
Lunch available/laundry facilities
Knowledgeable nature guides
DOC license WC 14098
Local features
Trout fishing, rainforest
Fiordland Crested Penguin
Seals

Wanaka - 3 hours drive
Hokitika - 3 hours 30 mins drive

The Lodge is located 30km north of Haast and 90km south of Fox Glacier on SH 6.

Wilderness Lodge Lake Moeraki is situated in the South West Coast's World Heritage Area. Walking into the lounge I was overwhelmed by the splendor of the view from the windows. The Lodge is surrounded by 1,000 year old rainforest trees and overlooks the Moeraki rapids. Owners Anne and Gerry set up the lodge to help protect the rainforests and share this extraordinary natural setting with visitors. Radiating from the lodge is a network of rainforest and Tasman Sea coast walks. The guides from the lodge will introduce you to crested penguins, fur seals, giant eels, unique birdlife and ancient forests. The comfortable accommodation includes rainforest rooms and superior river view rooms all beautifully furnished. After an exhausting but thrilling day out it was a pleasure to slide into one of the comfortable chairs in the Red Dog Saloon with a drink and watch the river roll by. Meals are served in the Riverside Restaurant and include great wilderness food, whitebait from the river, seafood from the coast, game from the forest, accompanied by an excellent wine list. The lodge, committed to the protection of the environment is an excellent example of New Zealand's Eco Tourism industry, not only in what it provides, but how it is provided.

Accommodation available (NZ$)	👤	👤👤	+👤	🛏	🛁	
12 Rooms	$300-350	$400-500		Q+S	EN	Breakfast: Special cooked
6 Rooms	$300-350	$400-500		Q	EN	Evening meal: Included
5 Rooms	$350-450	$500-700		K	EN	Guest rooms:
5 Rooms	$350-450	$500-700		Q+S	EN	Ambience:
						Setting/location:

Rippinvale Retreat

John and Helen Beattie
68 Rippingale Road, Hamner Springs
Tel: 03 3157139
Fax: 03 3157139   Free: 0800373098
rippinvale123@xtra.co.nz
www.lodgings.co.nz – keyword: rippinvale

Property features
Magnificient alpine views
2.5 acres landscaped gardens
Therapeutic swedish massage
Outdoor alpine jacuzzi
Pentanque/lawn tennis
Retreat gift packages
Local features
Famous thermal pools
4WD/walking treks
Hunting/fishing
Heli scenic flights

Hanmer Springs - 3 mins drive
Christchurch - 1 hr 40 mins drive

Rippinvale is on the edge of the township. Travel down Argelins Rd, second on left is Rippingale Rd. Follow our blue lodge sign.

Set among 2 ½ acres of stunning mature landscaped gardens, this exquisite Rippinvale Retreat provides magnificent alpine views and is elegantly situated on the western boundary of the Hanmer Springs golf course. Hosts John and Helen totally focus on the "guest experience", and after introductory orientation will quickly leave guests their own space. Both suites are stylishly furnished with all the comforts of modern day life, and opens out to an inviting private courtyard garden. Need to stretch out the kinks after all that Alpine driving? There's a lawn tennis court for the active, and petanque for the more sedentary. Maybe, before bed a hot soak is in order. There's a large outdoor alpine jacuzzi set amongst plantings. Sit, soak and contemplate the stars. And what stars! Hanmers altitude, providing notoriously crisp, clear air affords a star light panorama city dwellers cannot experience. Helen is a massage therapist and John offers guided hunting, camera stalking and mountain trekking. There are few better qualified to showcase the region. Before heading out for a fun packed day of activities, you must not miss the gourmet breakfast, condiments and preserves which are second to none! Only the freshest of New Zealand produce is used, much of which is home grown. It is a highlight at Rippinvale, one you will not forget!

Accommodation available (NZ$)	👤	👤👤	+👤	🛏	🛁	
2 Suites	$195-210	$295-355	$90	Q	EN	Breakfast: Special cooked

A top of the line settee is available in the sitting room of each suite.
Seasonal rates apply.

Guest rooms:
Ambience:
Setting/location:

LOW   HIGH

Property features

Spacious sunny rooms and suites
Breakfast at leisure in own suite
Quiet peaceful park like setting
Complimentary evening wine
Spa pool/billiard room
Centrally heated throughout

Local features

200m to thermal pools/restaurants
Massage & beauty therapy
Mountain biking/tramping
Golf/fishing/jetboating

Cheltenham House

Len and Maree Earl
13 Cheltenham Street, Hanmer Springs,
North Canterbury
Tel: 03 3157545
Fax: 03 3157645
enquiries@cheltenham.co.nz
www.lodgings.co.nz – keyword: cheltenham

Hanmer Springs - 2 mins walk
Christchurch - 1 hr 40 mins drive

When entering Hanmer Springs village pass the Thermal Pools and turn right into Cheltenham Street. Cheltenham House is a short way up on your right.

Built in colonial style, the Cheltenham experience is all about Hanmer history. Dating back to 1930 the house has been host to many kiwi notables over the years. Today, the house is a living history with, of course, the unobtrusive upgrades to advantage modern comforts and technology. Hosts Len and Maree have carefully preserved a wealth of artifact and photographs chronicling Hanmers early days. The Grandaughter of one of the original landowners built Cheltenham house and it was purchased by Len and Maree in 1995. The task of restoration was a daunting one but relished by both "We've set ourselves the task of providing a piece of living history. To furnish our suites, each named for an aspect or personality of house history, we've purchased and restored furnishings that have been around the Hanmer district since either the original settlers brought them or were locally made of native timber". It's not hard to meld with the past. Head for the guest lounge where there's a full sized billiard table illuminated with genuine antique height adjustable billiard lamps. Cue a few balls then close your eyes. Can't you see the group in the shadow there? Moleskins, white shirts, waistcoat! Yes, you are living history. Cheltenham house, a great place to enjoy the springs and the cafes and night life of Hanmer.

	Accommodation available (NZ$)	🧍	🧍🧍	+🧍	🛏	🛁
Family pets on site Guest pets by arrangement						
Breakfast: Cooked	1 Room	$160	$190	$50	Q+S	PR
	1 Room	$190	$220	$50	2Q	EN
Guest rooms:	2 Rooms	$200	$230		SK/T	EN
Ambience:	2 Studios	$170	$200		Q	EN
Setting/location:						

LOW   HIGH

The Charlotte Jane

Dee and Ani Reddy
110 Papanui Road, Merivale, Christchurch
Tel: 03 3551028
Fax: 03 3558882
Charjane@ihug.co.nz
www.lodgings.co.nz – keyword: thecharlottejane

Property features
Historic 19th century charm
Restaurant/garden
Library/wireless internet
Bar/wine cellar on site
Parking/dry cleaning/laundry
Local features
Botanical Gardens/Hagley Park
Merivale town centre
Merivale mall
Christchurch/Cathedral Square
Restaurants

Christchurch - 10 mins walk
Akaroa - 90 mins drive

From Christchurch city centre, follow Victoria Street (Parallel to North Hagley Park) until it turns into Papanui Road. The Charlotte Jane on the right hand side.

In the heart of Christchurch city, this exquisite five star grand Victorian mansion offers guest every luxury, service and comfort one could ask for. Upon arrival Dee my host showed me to my room. Wow, is the only word to describe. Each room is elegantly furnished in keeping with the grandeur of the mansion, and the attention to detail is outstanding, with comfortable beds, quality linen, artwork, and a grand fire place. The Charlotte Jane caters for all; the overseas travelers, business executives, and honeymooners, to name just a few. Complimentary pre dinner drinks are available in one of the two bars, where you can relax or socialize with the other guests. The onsite restaurant is set in a beautiful garden conservatory, with glass windows floor to ceiling. There is also a delightful outside area, with BBQ and grape vines overhanging the covered courtyard, perfect for those warm summer months, to enjoy the peacefulness and elegance of the outdoor gardens and night sky. Everything can be found at the Charlotte Jane, bar, library (with complimentary port and sherry), internet, conference facility, restaurant, outside verandahs. It is also in close proximity to all the finest restaurants, bars, shopping, botanical gardens, Cathedral Square, beaches and the many more attractions that Christchurch has to offer.

Accommodation available (NZ$)	♂	♂♂	+♂	🛏	🛁		
5 Rooms	$495			K	EN	Breakfast:	Special cooked
5 Rooms	$395			K	EN	Evening meal:	$60pp
1 Room	$495			K	EN	Guest rooms:	
1 Room	$350			K	EN	Ambience:	
1 Cottage	$695		$50	2D	EN	Setting/location:	

LOW   HIG

Property features
- Luxuious modern home
- Guest lounge with open fire
- Landscaped Avon River garden
- Flat screen TV in all rooms
- Courtesy drop off and pick ups

Local features
- Hagley Park/Botanical Garden - 3 mins
- Antartic Centre
- Trans Alpine train - 5 mins
- Akaroa - 1 hour
- Punting on the Avon

City Centre - 10 mins drive
Airport - 15 mins drive

Ambience-on-Avon

Helen and Lawson Little
45 Totara Street, Fendalton, Christchurch 8041
Tel: 03 3484537
Fax: 03 3484837   Free: 0800226628
contact@ambience-on-avon.co.nz
www.lodgings.co.nz – keyword: ambience

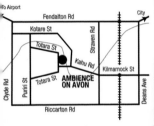

From Roundabout at Airport, take
second exit, Memorial Ave, turn right
at Clyde Rd, Left into Kotare St, first
right into Puriri St, first left into Totara
St, Ambience-on-Avon is on the left

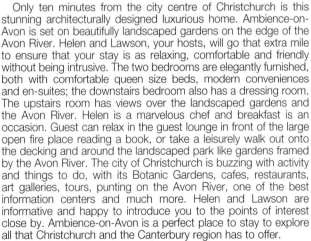

Only ten minutes from the city centre of Christchurch is this stunning architecturally designed luxurious home. Ambience-on-Avon is set on beautifully landscaped gardens on the edge of the Avon River. Helen and Lawson, your hosts, will go that extra mile to ensure that your stay is as relaxing, comfortable and friendly without being intrusive. The two bedrooms are elegantly furnished, both with comfortable queen size beds, modern conveniences and en-suites; the downstairs bedroom also has a dressing room. The upstairs room has views over the landscaped gardens and the Avon River. Helen is a marvelous chef and breakfast is an occasion. Guest can relax in the guest lounge in front of the large open fire place reading a book, or take a leisurely walk out onto the decking and around the landscaped park like gardens framed by the Avon River. The city of Christchurch is buzzing with activity and things to do, with its Botanic Gardens, cafes, restaurants, art galleries, tours, punting on the Avon River, one of the best information centers and much more. Helen and Lawson are informative and happy to introduce you to the points of interest close by. Ambience-on-Avon is a perfect place to stay to explore all that Christchurch and the Canterbury region has to offer.

Accommodation available (NZ$)	♦	♦♦	+♦	🛏	🛁
2 Rooms	$170-310	$200-340		Q	EN

Breakfast: Cooked

Guest rooms:
Ambience:
Setting/location:

LOW   HIGH

Seasonal rates apply, Wireless broadband available.

153

Hadleigh Heritage Home

Jon and Shirley Warring
6 Eversleigh St, Christchurch
Tel: 03 3557174   Mob: 0274972871
Fax: 03 3557174
info@hadleigh.co.nz
www.lodgings.co.nz – keyword: hadleigh

Property features
Category 2 historic listed home
Classic performance cars (Porsche)
Billiard & motorsport trophy room
Separate guest lounge
Small guest kitchenette
Arts & crafts style architecture
Local features
Botanical Gardens/Hagley Park
Arts Centre/casino
Punting on the Avon River
Antarctic Centre/Cathedral Square

City centre - 17 mins walk
Airport - 15 mins drive

Bealey Ave borders central
Christchurch to the north. From the
airport or north Hagley Park continue
along Bealey Ave and turn left into
Springfield Rd. Hadleigh is on the
corner of Eversleigh St on the right.

I love places that are full of character and history. This home, which is one of this country's best examples of the Arts and Crafts architectural style has been restored to the standard it deserves and is sympathetically furnished with a great deal of care. The four guest suites (two of which have two bedrooms) all have private bathrooms, comfortable seating, televisions, complimentary port and fresh flowers. They are spacious and well appointed. There is a small guest kitchen on the same level, where we could have made a light meal. The refrigerator was stocked with complimentary beverages and snacks. Jon and Shirley asked me to join them in the gracious sitting room, with its lattice bay windows overlooking the garden, for a drink before I went out for dinner. Jon has a specialised interest in Porsche racing and in order to house his three-car collection a facility of 150 square metres has been added to the house. I was welcome to explore the extensive gardens, to hone my skills in the billiard room, play the piano and peruse the small library. In the morning a full English-style breakfast was served with strawberries and peaches fresh from the potage garden.

Family dog on site

Accommodation available (NZ$)	🧍	🧍🧍	+🧍	🛏	🛁	
1 Suite	$252	$308	$52	Q+S	PR	Breakfast: Cooked
1 Suite	$290	$425		K/T	EN	
1 Suite	$260	$375		Q	EN	Guest rooms:
1 Suite	$316	$316	$52	K/T+Q	EN	Ambience:

Writing desk available in suite. Rates negotiable on 3-day plus stays.

Setting/location:

Property features
Complimentary sherry & port
min to Merivale shops/cafes
Separate guest lounge
Historic Places Trust classification
Period furnishings/DVD in rooms
Native timbers & leadlight windows

Local features
Hagley Park and gardens
Antique shops/casino
Punting on Avon River
Golf courses nearby

City centre - 10 mins drive
Dunedin - 4 hrs 30 mins drive

From north, continue on Main North
Rd rather than turning into Cranford
St (SH 74). Becomes Papanui Rd as
it veers left. From south turn left at
Hagley Park. Continue on to Harper
Ave and left into Papanui Rd.

Elm Tree House

Karen and Allan Scott
236 Papanui Road, Merivale, Christchurch
Tel: 03 3559731
Fax: 03 3559753
stay@elmtreehouse.co.nz
www.lodgings.co.nz - keyword: elmtree

For those of you not familiar with Christchurch, Merivale is a haven for cafes, restaurants, antique shops as well as conventional retail outlets. Elm Tree House is just a short stroll to them all and, despite the busy nature of this location, the property has a relaxed feel to it, as it is set back from the road in a large garden. This character home has a civilised 'club' atmosphere in the communal areas. The rooms vary in style. My favourite is the Honeymoon Suite with its heavy timber-panelling, writing desk and separate lounge area. The Cromwell and Milford Rooms are downstairs. They have polished floors and French doors that lead to their own small courtyards and gardens. Although the interesting 1920's architecture is a real feature here, the thing that sticks in my mind is the thought Karen and Allan have put into ensuring their guests' comfort. They are continually thinking of ways to improve it, such as installing double-glazing in all of the bedrooms to eliminate road noise. Happy hour, where complimentary wine and cheese are served in the new conservatory or the garden, lives up to its name and many guests say that a stay here feels like coming home.

Family dog on site

Breakfast: Special cooked

Guest rooms:
Ambience:
Setting/location:

Accommodation available (NZ$)	🧍	🧍🧍	+🧍	🛏	🛁
2 Rooms	$315	$345		K/T	EN
1 Room	$315	$345		K	EN
1 Room	$255	$285		K/T	EN
1 Room	$255	$285		Q	EN

A surcharge of NZD$30pp applies in the High Season.

155

Dyers House

Angela and Barry Hawkins
85 Dyers Pass Road, Cashmere, Christchurch
Tel: 03 3371675
Fax: 03 3371765
info@dyershouse.co.nz
www.lodgings.co.nz – keyword: dyershouse

Property features
Spectacular views
Renovated luxury accomodation
Double-glazing, under-floor heating
Courtesy transfers
Equisite décor
Local features
City centre - 10 mins
Botanic gardens/Art gallery
Restaurants/cafes
Golf courses/punting on Avon River
Sightseeing tours

Christchurch - 10 mins drive
Ashburton - 1 hour drive

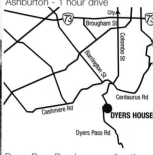

Dyers Pass Road comes directly off the hill end of Colombo street, which is the main central street in Christchurch. As a courtesy your hosts can meet you at the airport or railway station.

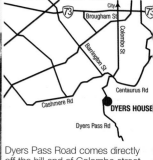

Set on the beautiful Cashmere Hills, Dyers House, one of Cashmere's oldest homes, has the most stunning views over Christchurch, the Canterbury plains, the Southern Alps and the ocean. This beautifully refurbished home offers 3 gorgeous rooms all exquisitely decorated with luxurious individual themes to suit the most discerning traveller. All rooms have wonderful views, a private balcony, double-glazing, underfloor heating, full insulation, TV, DVD, tea and coffee making facilities, and much more. The guest sitting room, library and dining room are all upstairs and surrounded by a spectacular balcony with views for miles, you will not be disappointed. The hosts Angela and Barry are most welcoming and nothing is a problem for them. Their knowledge and experience is second to none and it is a delight just to listen to their stories, also they can help you plan your sightseeing trips or activities. With so much happening in Christchurch, you will not be short of things to do. Botanic gardens, Victoria Park, art galleries, golf courses, punting on Avon River, award winning cafes/restaurants to name just a few. I must mention the two cats and elderly black Labrador, they are just a treat. Dyers House is the perfect luxurious place to stay to appreciate the beauty and history of Christchurch.

Accommodation available (NZ$)	👤	👤👤	+👤	🛏	🛁	Family pets on site
3 Rooms	$320	$320		Q	EN	Breakfast: Cooked

Evening meal available on request.

Guest rooms:
Ambience:
Setting/location:

LOW   HIG

Property features
Magnificent mountain & ocean views
Panoramic city views
Spa pool - outdoor
Tranquil rural setting

Local features
Port hills walking/mountain biking
Lyttleton - 10 mins
Akaroa - 1 hr 30 mins
Mt Hutt ski field - 1 hr 30 mins
Beach - 7 mins
Gondola - 10 mins
Christchurch - 20 mins drive
Akaroa - 1 hr 30 mins drive

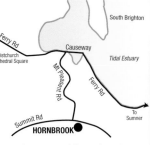

From city centre, follow signs to Sumner. Shortly after the road joins waterfront take Mt. Pleasant Rd on your right. Drive approx. 5.5km to Summit Rd T intersection. Hornbrook is immediately on left.

Hornbrook

Darryn and Jo Shepherd
Summit Road, Mt Pleasant, Christchurch
Tel: 03 3840020
Fax: 03 3840320
hornbrook@farmside.co.nz
www.lodgings.co.nz – keyword: hornbrook

Staying here is like being on top of the world in a quiet country location, and yet it is just a short drive to the city, Sumner Village and Lyttelton. The view from here is huge and takes in much of the city and South Shore, the estuary, and as far as the eye can see up the coast to the Seaward Kaikoura Mountains. This is a great area for walking the tracks and quiet roads of the Port Hills. I am told the walk to Sumner is not difficult but the walk back up is not for the faint hearted. The house has character and is laid out in such a way that you can either be sociable in the lounge, or sit quietly in the large dining room with its own sound system. A wall of glass doors opens to the front courtyard and garden where, under a vine-covered pergola, there is a spa pool and barbecue area. Darryn and Jo are happy to let guests take charge in this spacious and comfortable place, which was built in 1911 and named after the pioneer owner of the original Mt Pleasant sheep run. It was difficult to tear myself away from the view which took on different moods as the day advanced. Breakfast was a leisurely help-yourself affair with fresh fruit, cereals, yoghurt, toasts and juices.

Family cat on site

Breakfast: Continental

Guest rooms:
Ambience:
Setting/location:

Accommodation available (NZ$)	👤	👥	+👤	🛏	🛁
1 Room	$180	$180		K	EN
1 Room	$190	$190		K	EN

Seascape-Escape B&B

Colin and Gillian Needham
355 Mt Pleasant Road, Christchurch
Tel: 03 3848349   Mob: 021495549
Fax: 03 3848343
info@seascape-escape.co.nz
www.lodgings.co.nz – keyword: seascapeescape

(P) ✉ 📺 ✆

MasterCard VISA

Property features
Stunning sea views/1acre of land
Hot tub/kitchenette
Expansive decks/out door seating
Self contained/dinner on request
Spectacular sunrises

Local features
Gondola - 5 mins drive
Sumner beach - 5 mins drive
Hillside walks
Christchurch art centre - 20 mins
Akaroa - 1 hour drive

City centre - 20 mins drive
Airport - 30 mins drive

From central Christchurch follow Fitzgerald Ave, left into Ferry Rd towards Sumner, follow coast on to Main Rd, turn right into Mt Pleasant Rd, travel 3.4km. Seascape-Escape is on your left down a private road called The Terraces.

The Canterbury Plains are spread out before you from Seascape-Escape which is located high on the hills overlooking Sumner Beach. The view is extraordinary and so is Seascape Escape owned by Colin and Gillian Needham. On one acre of land, this luxurious two bedroom apartment is glorious with splendid attention to detail with under floor heating, kitchenette, high speed internet and own entrance. The furnishings are exquisite with bold splashes of colour to accent. The art works adorning the walls are the works of Colin and Gillian's very talented daughter Melissa. Guests can either breakfast on their own private patio or in the breakfast lounge upstairs which also has commanding views and art works. The gondola is a few minutes drive away and it is only 13km to the centre of Christchurch, renowned for its parks, architecture, art centre's and shopping. As an added bonus if you are shopping for that perfect gown then you may not have to move more than a few paces as Gillian is a designer of exquisite one off pieces. This talented family are passionate hosts and are happy to cater to your every need, gourmet dinners to kiwi BBQ. You will be very pleased that you made the journey up to the hills.

Accommodation available (NZ$)	🧍	🧍🧍	+🧍	🛏	🛁	Family cat on site
1 Suite	$350-700	$350-700		2K + 2S	PR	Breakfast: Cooked

Guest rooms:
Ambience:
Setting/location:

Tariff is for up to 4 people - other rates on application

Property features
Garden setting/stream/sea views
Fine dining and wines available
Open fire/Library/piano/stereo/CDs
Double spa bath with sea views
Private Lounge and decks
Under-floor heating in bathroom
Local features
Vintage car/Sidecar with Driver
Guided walks/dolphin swimming
Galleries and cruises
Golf incl club and trundler hire

Matua Gardens Retreat

Sue & Richard Lovett
15 Kingston Hill Road, Robinsons Bay, Akaroa
Tel: 03 3048946   Mob: 0274301131
Fax: 03 3048946
enquiry@matuagardens.co.nz
www.lodgings.co.nz – keyword: matuagardens

Akaroa - 10 mins drive
Christchurch - 1hr 15 mins drive

From Christchurch take SH75
towards Akaroa, at Robinsons Bay
turn left onto Robinsons Bay Valley
Rd. After 1 km, continue straight on
to Kingston Hill Road. Matua Gardens
Retreat is 70 Mtrs on the left.

The one hour drive out to Akaroa affords some of the best coastal views in Canterbury. Matua Gardens Retreat sits nestled in the valley above Robinsons Bay. With views out to the harbour this truly is a luxurious retreat. Comprising one queen bedroom, beautifully furnished complete with a decadent bath from which one can enjoy the view, right down to a choice of toiletries to suit the mood. We sat out on the deck enjoying the tranquil surroundings, nothing but the sound of the brook meandering past with the bird life in the trees, Grey Warblers and Bellbirds adding to the chorus. Extensive new plantings of native vegetation ensure continued sustainability. Sue and Richard are passionate hosts. Sue an excellent cook provides the option of a five course dinner with matched wines. As much as possible, local products are used, cheeses from down the road, salmon, wines and fruit and vegetables from the garden. Try the pickled walnuts and the blue. Dine either in the private lounge fireside or alfresco as the mood takes. The service is seamless. Sue and Richard live adjacent – somewhere. No request was too much trouble. The galleries, dolphins and cafes are just a short drive away however we found this the perfect place to rest up and be completely spoilt before heading home.

Accommodation available (NZ$)	👤	👥	+👤	🛏	🛁
1 Suite	$350	$395		Q	EN

Breakfast: Special cooked
Evening meal: Available
Guest rooms:
Ambience:
Setting/location:

Package price available for dinner/wines/bed and breakfast.

Maison de la Mer

Carol and Bruce Hyland
1 Rue Benoit, Akaroa, Banks Peninsula
Tel: 03 3048907   Mob: 021986221
Fax: 03 3048917
maisondelamer@xtra.co.nz
www.lodgings.co.nz – keyword: maison

(P) 人 12 ✉ 📺

Property features
Historic villa
Panoramic Harbour Views
Private Guest Lounge
French Country Décor
Wireless Internet / In room DVD
Local features
Harbour sailing
Dolphin watching/swimming
Historic village and country walks
French history museum
Vineyards

Akaroa - 1 mins walk
Christchurch - 1 hr 15 min drive

Maison de la Mer is situated in the heart of the village opposite the mai swimming beach on the corner of Rue Lavaud (main road) and Rue Benoit.

What a gem, located on a marvellous elevated waterfront position in the middle of Akaroa, Maison de la Mer overlooks the picturesque harbour. This graceful 1910 house has been restored with French country influences to reflect its original elegant standard. Soothing natural colours blend with antiques, Persian carpets and art collected from the hosts, Carol and Bruce's travels around the world combine to make Maison de la Mer a truly memorable place from which to explore this unique history entrenched area. The two luxurious bedrooms, have their own elegant style with stunning views over the harbour or choose the nautically themed boathouse. Nothing has been spared. Carol and Bruce are keen yachties and we sat with a drink watching the fishing boats coming and going as dusk descended chatting about their experiences and the history of this old French whaling port. Up with the dawn we started the day with one of their sumptuous breakfasts before exploring the walks and bird life on the peninsula. Other suggestions were roving around the galleries and cafés, viewing the dolphins or just retiring to the guest lounge with its luxurious leather couches in front of the fire with a book from their library. Maison de la Mer, truly a home by the sea.

Accommodation available (NZ$)	👤	👤👤	+👤	🛏	🛁	Family dog on site
1 Suite	$345	$345		Q + S	EN	Breakfast: Cooked
1 Suite	$345	$345		Q	EN	
1 S/C unit	$395	$395		K	EN	Guest rooms:
			$75			Ambience:

One room has spa bath.

Setting/location:

Property features
- Swiss-born fully trained chef
- Cooking classes by arrangement
- Guest lounge, openfire, library
- Dine at separate tables
- On site parking/helipad

Local features
- Terrace Downs golf course on site
- Rakaia Gorge/Peak Hill walkways
- Skiing Mt Hutt, Porter Heights
- Hot air ballooning Methven
- Jet boating/mountain bikes

Christchurch -1 hours drive
Mt Hutt - 25 mins drive

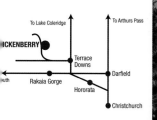

From Christchurch take SH73 towards Arthur's Pass, at Darfield turn left on to H77 and follow it until Windwhistle. Turn right towards Lake Coleridge for 4km and drive into Terrace Downs resort then take the first road on the right. Quickenberry is on the right.

Quickenberry

Christine and Robert Koller
Terrace Downs Golf Resort, Rakaia Gorge, Canterbury
Tel: 03 3186566
Fax: 03 3186566   Free: 0800318656
quickenberry@xtra.co.nz
www.lodgings.co.nz – keyword: quickenberry

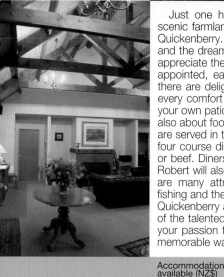

Just one hour's easy drive west from Christchurch through scenic farmland you will find the Terrace Downs Golf Resort and Quickenberry. This purpose built home is the result of Swiss design and the dream of Christine and Robert who are well traveled and appreciate the finer things in life. The four rooms are all beautifully appointed, each with its own characteristic theme. Everywhere there are delightful personal touches to ensure that the travelers every comfort is met. Retire to the library, the guest lounge or to your own patio and take in the mountain scenery. Quickenberry is also about food, Robert is an extraordinary chef. Pre-dinner drinks are served in the lounge around the fireplace before a magnificent four course dinner which may feature the finest Canterbury lamb or beef. Diners are seated at their own tables in fine dining style. Robert will also give cooking classes by prior arrangement. There are many attractions in the Mt Hutt area, skiing, jet boating, fishing and the golf course to name a few but essentially we found Quickenberry a superb place to unwind, enjoy the great company of the talented hosts and the fine dining experience. If food is not your passion then you are missing a truly wonderful occasion. A memorable way to start your South Island experience.

Accommodation available (NZ$)	👤	👤👤	+👤	🛏	🛁
4 Rooms	$250	$300-400		K or 2S	EN

Breakfast: Special cooked
Evening meal: included
Guest rooms:
Ambience:
Setting/location:

LOW   HIGH

4 course dinner included in the tariff

Grasmere Lodge

Tom Butler
SH 73, Cass, Canterbury
Tel: 03 3188407
Fax: 03 3188263
retreat@grasmere.co.nz
www.lodgings.co.nz – keyword: grasmere

Property features
Day Spa/Eco tours/guided hiking
Horse riding/ trout fishing/kayaks
Scenic flights/mountain biking
Gymnasium/tennis courts/petanque
Extensive library/swimming pool
Local features
Arthur's Pass National Park
Trout fishing/hunting/clay shooting
Four wheel drive to the back county
Ski Fields/airfield/helipad
Three lakes/Castle Hill Rocks

Christchurch - 1hr 30 mins drive
Arthur's Pass - 25 mins drive

From Christchurch take Yaldhurst Rc
SH 73, follow the signs for Arthur's Pa
until you reach Springfield, Grasme
is 45 mins past Springfield. Fr
Westcoast take SH 73 through Arthu
Pass, 30km on the right.

Grasmere is a destination. While it might be situated at the gateway to the Southern Lake Districts and the West Coast this magnificent 1500 acre property bordering Arthur's Pass National Park is an experience not to be missed. Our suite, the Riverview Cottage complete with fireplace, lounge, library/media room, kitchen and indulgent spa bath all looking out to stunning views of the mountains was the perfect place to watch the sun go down. No need to lift a finger here, nature paints its own art. And that was just the beginning. A tour of the property revealed the pool adjacent to the underground wine cellar - a summer haven, gym, trout pools, mountain bikes, walking and hiking trails, tennis, horse riding and much more. After all that activity, there is the spa offering an extensive array of treatments. Grasmere, though is also about people, and we joined fellow guests for pre diner drinks in the lodge before a gourmet dinner. A wonderful time to swap stories and plan for another day. Our host Tom and his staff could not have been more helpful. Another bonus, the Tranz Alpine Express, one of the world's great excursions runs by the far end of the property and staff are happy to meet you. There are some places that you go in life that you know that you have to return to and Grasmere is one of those.

Accommodation available (NZ$)	👤	👥	+👤	🛏	🛁	
						Family dog on site
						Guest pets by arrangement
6 rooms	$1165-1755	$1400-1755		K or 2S	EN	Breakfast: Special cooked
3 Suites	$1496-1820	$1755-2070	$439	K or 2S	EN	Evening meal: Included
2 Cottage 2Br	$1812	$2070-3825	$518	K or 2S	EN's	Guest rooms:
						Ambience:

Tariff includes pre dinner drinks, 5 course dinner and full cooked breakfast.

Setting/location:

LOW   HI

Property features
- Award winning restaurant on site
- Luxurious accommodation
- Open fires/spa and claw baths
- Private balconies
- Glass of champagne, fruit & choc platter
- Sheltered courtyard ideal for weddings

Local features
- Vineries/trout fishing/hunting/art galleries
- Museums/skiing/tramping/golf
- White water rafting
- Deserted beaches/great walks

Kavanagh House

David and Michelle Beer
State Highway One, Winchester, South Canterbury
Tel: 03 6156150
Fax: 03 6159694
info@kavanaghhouse.co.nz
www.lodgings.co.nz – keyword: kavanagh

Geraldine - 5 mins drive
Temuka - 5 mins drive

On State highway 1 at Winchester, 1.5 hours South of Christchurch.

Winchester, on SH1, south of Christchurch, locates Kavanagh house. It's a boutique lodge in a classical contemporary style offering a feeling of spacious exclusivity. Built in 1903 as the districts grand house, high ornately plastered ceilings and warm native wood floors remain to delight today. Set in glorious gardens, the house does make a grand statement. The great room incorporates relaxed dining, fireside lounge and friendly bar. Summer evenings, an embracing courtyard beckons. "We are seen as a romantic getaway for busy city folk, and our rooms are themed with romance in mind" comments Michelle. With luxury worthy of Hollywood's great era, the Rococco room is set with claw-footed baths, whilst the New York room boast a modern spa. Soak away the days tensions whilst sipping complimentary champagne and admiring the immaculately restored hand painted ceiling. No hurry, Kavanagh's award winning restaurant awaits with a menu to suit the discerning. "Dining is so important in the guest experience", says Michelle. As for activities we are spoilt for choice. The area has skiing, jet boating and rafting for the adventurous. Golfing maybe, or quiet lake, forest and beach walks. Indeed Kavanagh House makes a great getaway.

Family cat on site
Guest pets by arrangement

Breakfast: Special cooked
Evening meal: $30-40pp

Guest rooms:
Ambience:
Setting/location:

Accommodation available (NZ$)	👤	👤👤	+👤	🛏	🛁
1 Room	$250	$320		K	EN
1 Room	$220	$295		Q	EN

LOW   HIGH

Kingsdown Manor

Peter and Rochelle Young
10 Bristol Road, RD 1 Kingsdown, Timaru
Tel: 03 6849612   Mob: 0272011316
Fax: 03 6849613
info@kingsdownmanor.co.nz
www.kingsdownmanor.co.nz
www.lodgings.co.nz – keyword: kingsdown

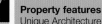

  12

Property features
Unique Architecture - English/Gothic
Fully licenced, dinner by arrangemen
Private dining room/guest lounge
Chapel on site
Landscaped grounds
Local features
Museum/art gallery - 5 mins
Local vineyards
Penguin colony/Maori rock art
Golf courses/Caroline Bay
White water rafting/horse treking

Timaru - 5 mins drive
Christchurch - 2 hours drive

From Timaru, travel south on SH1 fe
6.5km, turn right into Bristol Road.
Main entrance 100m from corner.

   Located just 6km south of Timaru with all the grandeur reminiscent of an English Country Manor. With its distinctive turret and interesting architecture, you will find yourself surrounded in olde world charm and ambience. Built around an old country chapel (circa 1905), the property offers the discerning traveler a truly unique experience as you enjoy the individually themed suites, the lodge like guest lounge with its plush leather settees and cosy open fire, or the wonderful rural views from the outdoor courtyard and garden area. Timaru is emerging as a destination for those travelers who choose to take the SH 1coastal route to see the South Island and the Manor is the perfect stopover, being an easy 2hr drive from both Christchurch and Dunedin cities. It also offers a very central location to explore the lakes and surrounding districts that offer a wide selection of activities   such as white water rafting, horse trekking, hunting safaris and vineyard tours etc. The region boasts more golf courses per captia than anywhere in New Zealand and the local rivers offer excellent fly and trout fishing opportunities. Your hosts, Peter, Rochelle, Stevie and Ben Young are all born and bred Southlanders and offer that true "southern hospitality" and genuine kiwi experience to those sharing their home.

Accommodation available (NZ$)	👤	👤👤	+👤	🛏	🛁	Family pets on site
1 Suite	$150	$250		K	EN	Breakfast: Cooked
1 Suite	$150	$230		Q	EN	Evening meal: $30pp
1 Suite	$150	$180	$60	Q + 1S	PR	Guest rooms:
						Ambience:
Evening meals by arrangement.						Setting/location:

LOW   HIG

Property features
Stunning lake/alpine views
Local photography
Garden
Hand-embroidered bed linen
Hospitality hour
Local features
Earth & Sky Observatory
Alpine winter park & hot pools
Scenic flights
Walking trails
Lake cruises

Lake Tekapo -15 mins walk
Timaru - 1 hour 25 mins drive

From north (Christchurch) take
1st turn on left onto Hamilton Dr
just before lookout). Grandview
is the 1st house on the left
400m from SH8. From the south
Queenstown) drive through the
village and cross the bridge, take
2nd right 800m from bridge onto
Hamilton drive.

Lake Tekapo Grandview

Leon and Rosemary O'Sullivan
32 Hamilton Drive, Lake Tekapo
Tel: 03 6806910   Mob: 0211113393
Fax: 03 6806912
info@laketekapograndview.co.nz
www.lodgings.co.nz – keyword: grandview

The property certainly has views worthy of its name. Grandview was built on an elevated site with stunning panoramic lake and alpine vistas. The accommodation was purpose built in 2002 and has four good-sized rooms with king-size beds and ensuites. Three rooms have decks and, after the long drive to get here, I enjoyed relaxing al fresco with a cup of tea. Drinks and hors d'oeuvres were served in the early evening, which gave me the chance to meet other guests and to get to know my hosts. Leon and Rosemary both come from New Zealand farming backgrounds and were pleased to share their knowledge of the land with me. They take a big interest in their guests, even tracking where they come from on a world map that hangs in the entrance to the house. It was an easy walk from the property into town where there were several restaurants to choose from. On the walk home I took a moment to enjoy the night sky. It was a very still, clear night, and because of the lack of city lights, a myriad of stars were visible in all their glory.

Accommodation available (NZ$)	🧍	🧍🧍	+🧍	🛏	🛁
1 Room		$295		SK	EN
1 Room		$270		K	EN
1 Room		$270		K	EN
1 Room		$240	$40	SK + S	EN

Breakfast: Special cooked

Guest rooms:
Ambience:
Setting/location:

LOW   HIGH

165

Matuka Lodge

Rosalie and Russell Smith
Old Station Road, Twizel
Tel: 03 4350144
Fax: 03 4350149
info@matukalodge.co.nz
www.lodgings.co.nz – keyword: matukalodge

Property features
Spectacular mountain views
Exclusive accommodation
Private pond with trout
Peace and tranquility
Excellent dining
Local features
Aoraki/Mt Cook - 45 mins
Heli flight-seeing
Bushwalking in Mt Cook National Park
Fly fishing
Endangered black stilt program

Twizel - 5 mins drive
Queenstown - 2 hrs 30 mins drive

Approaching Twizel from the North, on Inland Scenic Route 8, cross the Twizel River, turn right into Glen Lyo Road, travel 3km then left into Old Station Road.

Set among spectacular scenery deep in the heart of the South Island's Mackenzie Country, Matuka Lodge is luxury accommodation and has some of the best fly-fishing in New Zealand close by. Anyone who stays here is fortunate. The lodge is elegant and intimate with an ambience created by original artworks and antiques blending with contemporary furniture. My suite had a king-size bed, individual climate control, mountain views and a verandah that overlooked a large ornamental pond. In the ensuite bathroom was under-floor heating, a heated, towel rail and cosy bathrobes. I was woken in the morning by the sun streaming in my window and had breakfast on the main deck that leads off the lounge and extends out over the pond. Trout swam lazily by. I didn't want to leave this peaceful haven but Rosalie and Russell had recommended a tour to the natural wonderland of nearby Aoraki/Mt Cook National Park. After an action-packed day, I came back to a pre-dinner drink on the deck. On the menu that night were fresh salmon and venison accompanied by delicious wine. Matuka opens all summer but is sometimes closed in the winter. It's an ideal place to stop on the way from Christchurch to Queenstown.

Accomodation available (NZ$)	🧍	🧍🧍	+🧍	🛏	🛁
1 Room	$380	$425		K	EN
1 Room	$450	$495		SK	EN

Breakfast: Cooked
Evening meal: $70pp
Guest rooms:
Ambience:
Setting/location:

Lodge is open all year.

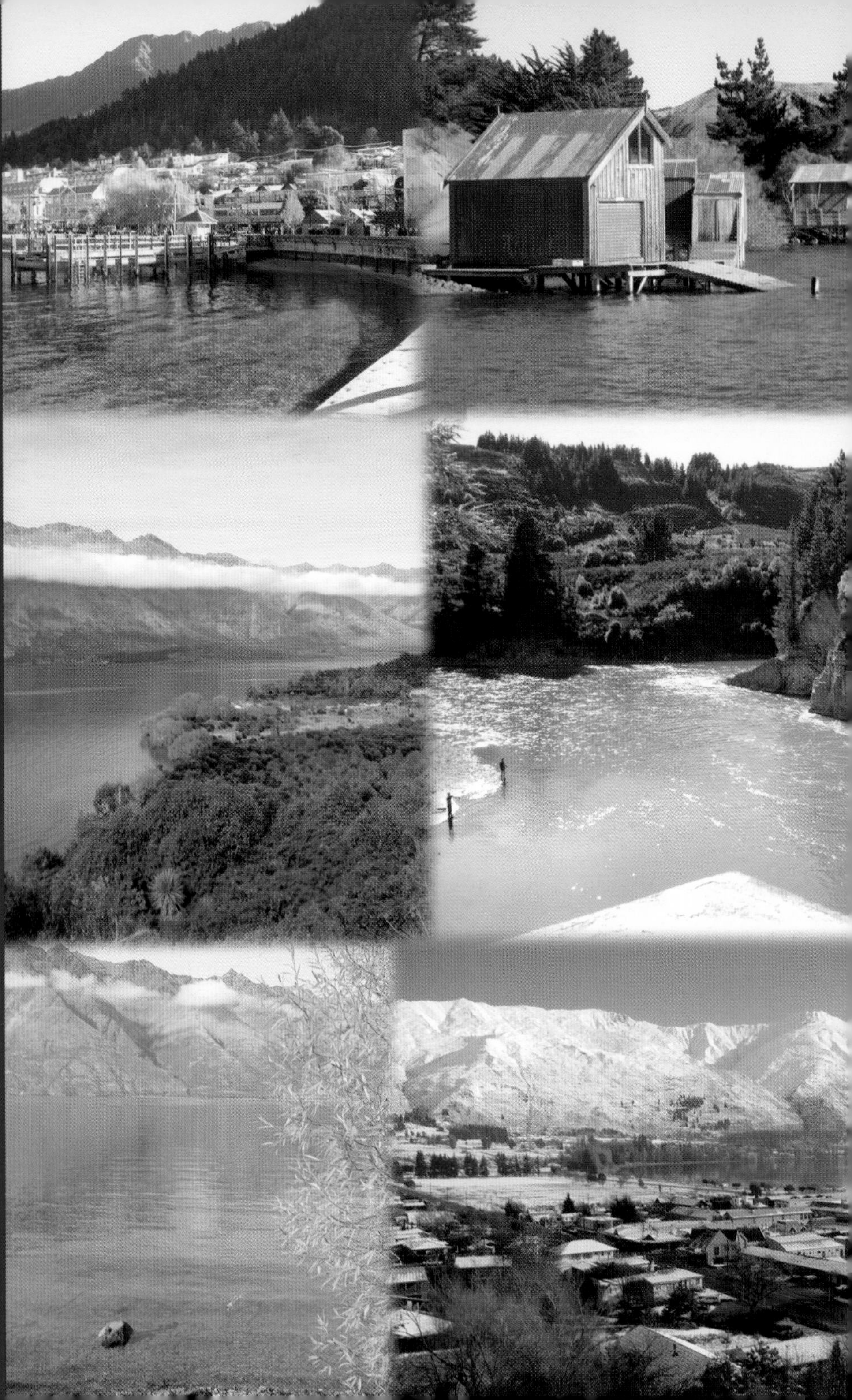

Pen-y-bryn Lodge

Roy and Bernice Vannini
41 Towey Street, Oamaru
Tel: 03 4347939
Fax: 03 4349063
admin@penybryn.co.nz
www.lodgings.co.nz – keyword: penybryn

Property features
Award winning heritage lodge
honeymoons/weddings
Genuine slate billiards table
Log fires/fine dining
Local features
Penguin viewing - 5 mins
Golf courses - 5 mins
Oamaru public gardens
Harbour & Tyne historic precinct
Dunedin Albatross colony
Fishing/scenic flights

Oamaru - Central
Dunedin - 1 hour drive

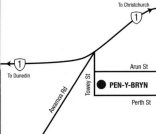

Pen-y-bryn is on the Southern out skirts of Oamaru. From South turn right into Towey St from SH1 at Y Junction with Awamoa Rd. From North turn left at Y Junction 100m on right.

Drive up to Pen-y-Bryn Lodge, its impressive, large imposing yet welcoming with beautiful gardens. Step inside however and you know that this is a very special part of New Zealand history. I felt privileged to share this with current owners Roy and Bernice our New Zealand hosts. The home built in the 1880's- the generations have preserved and protected this national treasure. The carved wood paneling, artworks, and extraordinary fine furniture add to the ambience. The two bedrooms in the house are characterised by original fixtures, with all the luxuries to make our stay exceptional. There are a further three rooms in the annex over looking the original garden and potager, that have been furnished in keeping with the house. With a maximum of 10 guests, you are sure to be spoilt. Pre-dinner drinks are served in the candlelit dining room before being seated at the table set with the finest of crystal and cutlery. It all about fine food, prepared by Bernice using the freshest of produce. While this is a magnificent place for any occasion, I asked Roy and Bernice what was the special thing about their home and they replied "Roy and Bernice". They are right. Surrounded by the beauty of this home these wonderful hosts are the perfect guardians of history and you will leave feeling like a part of the family.

Accommodation available (NZ$)	👤	👤👤	+👤	🛏	🛁	Family cat on site
4 Rooms	$557-620	$889-1012		Q	EN	Breakfast: Special cooked
1 Room	$557-620	$889-1012		K or 2S	EN	Evening meal: Included

Tarriff includes pre-dinner drinks, five course table d'hôte dinner, bed and full breakfast. Seasonal rates apply

Guest rooms:
Ambience:
Setting/location:

LOW   HIGH

Property features
Ten acres of landscaped grounds
Uninterrupted mountain views
Swimming pool/spa pool
Pitch and putt golf course (5 holes)
Helipad
Stylish guest lounge with open fire
Local features
Mt Aspiring National Park/hiking
Treble Cone/Cardrona ski resorts
Lake activities/trout fishing/kayaking
Scenic flights/vineyards/golf

Lime Tree Lodge

Sally Carwardine Rebecca Butts
672 Ballantyne Road, Wanaka
Tel: 03 4437305   Mob: 021529118
Fax: 03 4437345
revive@limetreelodge.co.nz
www.lodgings.co.nz – keyword: limetree

Wanaka - 6 mins drive
Queenstown - 1 hour drive

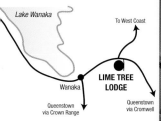

From Wanaka town centre travel
approximately 6km towards
Cromwell on SH6. Lime Tree Lodge
is on the corner of Ballantyne Road
just past the West Coast turn-off.

Lime Tree Lodge has undergone an extensive, interior makeover and I was enchanted with the results which far exceeded any expectations I'd had from the outside of this purpose-built building. Sally and Rebecca have put their hearts and souls into this property and the result is a lodge that manages to be both sophisticated and unpretentious - very easy to relax in, but still with all modern conveniences and luxuries. Four of the guestrooms open to a patio, an expansive lawn and a large pool area. Beyond are the mountains, and their changing moods became a big part of the experience of staying here. Among the six rooms, two new, ultra-modern suites, called Black Peak and Linden, are extravagant in detail. Sally and Rebecca have thought of everything. I favoured Black Peak suite because it has a log fire, a private terrace and great views of the mountains. There are other excellent facilities for guest use, such as a swimming pool, spa pool, a five-hole pitch-and-putt golf course and a helipad. The lodge is only six kilometres from Wanaka but because it is set on ten acres of land, it feels well away from the busy world.

Accomodation available (NZ$)	👤	👤👤	+👤	🛏	🛁
1 Room	$330-375	$350-395		Q	EN
3 Rooms	$330-375	$350-395		K, SK or 2S	EN
1 Suite	$430-475	$450-495		SK or 2S	EN
1 Suite	$530-575	$550-595	$75	SK or 2S+2S	EN

Breakfast: Cooked
Evening meal: $95pp
Guest rooms:
Ambience:
Setting/location:

LOW   HIGH

Wireless internet access available.

Maple Lodge

Paul and Bernadette Raymont
Halliday Road, Wanaka
Tel: 03 4436275   Mob: 021514868
Fax: 03 4436274
enquiries@maplelodgewanaka.co.nz
www.lodgings.co.nz – keyword: maplelodge

(P) 人人 12 ✉ ♿   MasterCard VISA eftpos

Property features
Luxurious guest suites with private patio
Guest lounge with log fire
7 acre maple tree plantation
Spa and petanque
Splendid mountain views
Local features
Lake Wanaka and Mount Aspiring
4 skiing areas
Boating/fishing/walking
Wineries

Wanaka - 4 mins drive

From the centre of Wanaka take the main highway to Cromwell for 3km turn left into Halliday Road, 500m turn right into Maple Lodge.

Situated on 2.5 hectares of rural land on the outskirts of Wanaka, Maple Lodge is a brand-new, 7-bedroom complex, with outstanding views of the mountains. Rooms are individually furnished and named after New Zealand native trees. As the name implies, Maple Lodge is surrounded by a plantation of Maple trees, which will form the basis of an arboretum. Our hosts, Berny and Paul have designed a striking building, utilizing schist and recycled timber. The centrepiece is a large common room, opening out to a paved courtyard and oozes style, warmth, and character, enhanced by a large stone open fireplace. The ideal place to relax with a glass of the famous local pinot noir, after a great day on the ski slopes. Breakfast served in a communal dining area consists of a continental option, plus a full cooked selection, which is varied from day to day. Paul and Berny want their guests to enjoy unobtrusive, homely, affordable luxury, without the necessity to leave the property. To this extent, they provide outdoor games, petanque and their own "Lord of the Rings" game, plus a luxurious spa to ease those travel aches and pains. I can recommend Maple Lodge as the perfect place to stay for a few days and rejuvenate. Surround yourself with luxury and enjoy the wonderful activities to be found in the Lake Wanaka region.

Accommodation available (NZ$)	👤	👥	+👤	🛏	🛁	Family dog on site
2 Rooms	$250	$335	$85	K	EN	Breakfast: Special cooked
2 Rooms	$210	$295		SK or 2S	EN	Evening meal: Enquire
3 Rooms	$210	$295		K	EN	Guest rooms:
						Ambience:

Seasonal rates may apply

Setting/location:

RECOMMENDED ★★★★★ BOUTIQUE LODGINGS   LOW   HIGH

Property features
Croquet and petanque
Lunch hampers - by arrangement
Complimentary pre-dinner drinks
Guest pick-up available
Mountain bikes available
Feature garden
Local features
Skifields
Golf course
Fishing/lakeside walks
Jet boating/kayaking

The Stone Cottage

Belinda Wilson
Dublin Bay, Wanaka
Tel: 03 4431878
Fax: 03 4431276
stonecottage@xtra.co.nz
www.lodgings.co.nz – keyword: stonecottage

Wanaka - 10 mins drive
Queenstown - 1 hour drive

From Wanaka, drive 4km towards Lake Hawea / West Coast on SH 6, then turn left into Dublin Bay Rd. The Stone Cottage is near the end of the road on your left.

Although the Stone Cottage is just a short drive from Wanaka, I could easily have imagined I was marooned on an island. The proximity to the lake and the magnificent view are important features of staying here. The view extends across the lake to Treble Cone ski field and, if the timing is right, you might be able to lie in bed at night and see the lights of the snow groomers on the mountains in the distance. The two suites occupy the upper level of Belinda's home and are accessed independently by staircases at each end of the building. The larger suite has more substantial facilities, such as a full stove, and French doors leading to a balcony taking full advantage of the view. The smaller suite is newer; it also takes in the views and has an outdoor table and chairs on the landing - great for an alfresco breakfast. If you're are travelling on your own opt for the smaller suite; with others in tow, an adjoining door can be opened to create a 'super-suite', with loads of living space. Belinda loves to 'play' in the kitchen so you would be well advised to eat in. A visitor from Hong Kong wrote: 'So there is a heaven on earth! The silence and solitude are unbelievable. Thanks a million.'

Family dog on site	Accomodation available (NZ$)	🧍	🧍🧍	+🧍	🛏	🛁
	1 Studio	$220	$250-280		SK	EN
	1 Apartment	$220	$280-300	$50	D+2S	EN

Breakfast: Special cooked
Evening meal: $65pp
Guest rooms:
Ambience:
Setting/location:

173

Mountain Range Boutique Lodge

Melanie Laaper Stuart Pinfold
Heritage Park, Cardrona Valley Road, Wanaka
Tel: 03 4437400
Fax: 03 4437450
stay@mountainrange.co.nz
www.lodgings.co.nz – keyword: mountainrange

Property features
8-seater cedar hot tub
Cosy guest lounge with open fire
DVD/Sky TV
Complimentary wireless internet
Home-baked afternoon tea daily
Local features
Mt Aspiring National Park
Golf course/putting green
Ski fields - 20 mins
Spectacular day walks/hiking
Fishing/boating

Wanaka - 2 mins drive
Queenstown - 1 hour drive

From West Coast or ChCh, take SH 84 towards Wanaka. Follow lake front and turn left into Macdougall Street. Heritage Park is approx 2 km on the left. Once in the park Mountain Range is on the left.

Mountain Range Boutique Lodge is a ranch-style lodge set on ten acres of parkland at the foot of the ranges from which it takes its name. Even though it's only a two-minute drive from the township, the property is surrounded by open space and is overlooked by the dramatic peaks of the rugged mountains. I was made very welcome and in the afternoon, I relaxed in front of a roaring, open fire before the thought of a soak in the Canadian cedar hot tub, which is set in the native garden, got the better of me. In the evening I took a 'trip' around the Southern Hemisphere's night sky through a telescope that is made available to guests. The rooms are presented with an understated elegance. All have spacious ensuites, and luxurious beds and they open onto private verandahs with spectacular views. Stuart and Melanie are young, outdoor enthusiasts who are well travelled and they are generous with their hospitality. I don't play golf but for those who do there is a course right next door and Stuart joins his guests for a round when he has time. Mountain Range is a stylish and comfortable retreat and a great base from which to explore the Wanaka region.

Accommodation available (NZ$)	👤	👤👤	+👤	🛏	🛁	
1 Room	$205-245	$220-315		SK	EN	Breakfast: Special cooked
6 Rooms	$205-245	$200-285		SK or 2S	EN	

Guest rooms:
Ambience:
Setting/location:

LOW   HIGH

Property features
Lake and mountain views
Separate guest dining & lounge
Award winning garden
Overlooking wildlife reserve
Local features
Skifields - 20 minutes
Several golf courses nearby
Restaurants/cafes - 5 minutes
Day tours Milford/Doubtful Sound
Vineyards/wineries - 2 minutes

The Turret

James and Kim Lazor
Lake Hayes, Queenstown
Tel: 03 4421107
theturret@xtra.co.nz
www.lodgings.co.nz – keyword: turret

Arrowtown - 5 mins drive
Queenstown - 15 mins drive

From Queenstown, take SH 6
towards Cromwell approx. 12km,
The Turret is on your right. From
Cromwell / Wanaka continue past
the second Arrowtown turnoff. The
Turret is on your left.

James and Kim are the hosts of this charming lodge and, when I met them, the first thing I noticed was the depth of their life experience. I was warmly welcomed to share a glass of wine in the sunny living room overlooking the lovely front garden and Lake Hayes. This is a house of strong character with a lively and inviting ambience, which is impossible not to enjoy. If you are looking for time by yourself, there are some wonderful enclaves on the patio, in the beautifully landscaped garden, or on the nearby Lake Hayes walking track. The front door of the house opens to the guest dining area and adjacent is a quiet and cosy guest-dedicated living room dominated by a large open fireplace. Downstairs two attractive bedrooms open to the patio and a tranquil outlook over Lake Hayes and up to Coronet Peak. But the piece de resistance is the large turret suite upstairs, which, with its elegant décor, walk-in change room and spacious bathroom with shower and a claw foot bath, is like a room in a palace. In the attached turret is a intriguingly decorated, private sitting room with a stunning view. This house is different and very interesting and a great base from which to explore the district.

Accommodation available (NZ$)	👤	👤👤	+👤	🛏	🛁
1 Room	$200	$220		2S or 1K	PR
1 Room	$210	$230-350		Q	EN
1 Suite	$325	$345-450	$25	Q	EN

Breakfast: Cooked

Guest rooms:
Ambience:
Setting/location:

175

Pencarrow

Bill and Kari Moers
678 Frankton Rd, Queenstown
Tel: 03 4428938   Mob: 0274131567
Fax: 03 4428974
info@pencarrow.net
www.lodgings.co.nz – keyword: pencarrow

(P) 🚶 12 ✉ 📺 ☎

Property features
Lake and mountaiin views
All rooms are large suites
Enormous ensuite bathrooms
Outdoor spa/garden/fireplace
Double vanity/spa baths
Sky TV/mini bar/internet
4 course breakfast/4 acres

Local features
Wineries/jetboating/skiing
Day tours Milford/Doubtful Sound
Hike/golf/fishing/rafting

Queenstown - 5 mins drive
Arrowtown - 15 mins drive

Take 6A (Frankton Rd) towards Queenstown. After the Shell Petrol Station travel 1.2km and turn right into Greenstone Terrace Apartments. Take private drive straight ahead up hill to Pencarrow.

Located just on the outskirts this modern lodge is not far from Queenstown centre. Pencarrow, named after New Zealand's first lighthouse, is perched on a hillside overlooking Lake Wakatipu and the Remarkables Mountains. Bill and Kari were warmly welcoming. The couple have been in the hospitality industry for some time and both are well versed in the small details that add to guests' comfort. At one side of the entrance to the lodge is a spa pool and outdoor fire. I made a mental note to spend time there later in the evening. My suite was the complete package with plenty of space, a king-size bed, a huge bathroom with a spa bath, and a selection of products to enjoy. Before I went into town to find dinner I had a game of snooker in the 'games room', as Bill and Kari call it. Here there are also darts, books and photos and other entertainment. Pencarrow, with its four large suites, is well proportioned and warmed by colours that have been carefully chosen to enhance the interiors. A country breakfast is served in the dining room, on an outdoor terrace or deck, or in your own suite. You'll be spoiled by the hosts at this five star property.

Accommodation available (NZ$)	🧍	🧍🧍	+🧍	🛏	🛁	
1 Suite		$495-585	$75	K	EN	Breakfast: Special cooked
3 Suites		$495-585	$75	SK	EN	

Guest rooms:
Ambience:
Setting/location:

LOW   HIGH

Property features
Mountain views
Large lounge/private library
Close proximity to town/gondola
Open fireplace/central heating
Ski storage/hydrotherapy spa
Cooked breakfasts/afternoon teas
Local features
Skifields - 30 min drive
Tramping/nature walks
Scenic flights/fishing/jetboating
Vineyards/wineries - 30 min

The Dairy, Private Luxury Hotel
Elspeth Zemla
Corner Isle and Brecon Streets, Queenstown
Tel: 03 4425164
Fax: 03 4425166   Free: 0800333393
info@thedairy.co.nz
www.lodgings.co.nz - keyword: thedairy

Queenstown - 1 mins walk
Arrowtown - 15 mins drive

THE DAIRY PRIVATE LUXURY HOTEL

Entering Queenstown on SH 6A,
continue along Stanley St to 2nd
roundabout. Here go straight, the road
bends sharply left. Continue straight
at next roundabout onto Man St. Turn
right into Brecon St. The Dairy is on
the corner of Isle and Brecon Sts.

If you want to stay in the heart of Queenstown but out of the way of the noise, this private luxury hotel suits perfectly. There are thirteen rooms, many of which have views of the Remarkables Mountain Range. The hotel was refurbished and offers contemporary comfort with items such as silk cushions, mohair rugs and superb linen. The Dairy takes its name from the original 1920's corner store, and exudes a timeless elegance. The large guest lounge is comfortable and is decorated with style. It boasts generous leather couches and is warmed by the roaring open fire. It was a perfect place to unwind and one that I could imagine guests sitting and sharing travelling tales. Throughout The Dairy, old New Zealand product, packaging and dairy items hint at its past. A highlight for me was afternoon tea where delicious home baked goods, which The Dairy has become renowned for, were available. This is an ideal place from which to experience all the activities in the area. The hosts make recommendations for restaurants, services and tourist operators, and will book them if guests wish.

Accommodation available (NZ$)	👤	👤👤	+👤	🛏	🛁
8 Rooms	$410	$440		SK/T	EN
3 Rooms	$380	$410		SK/T	EN
2 Rooms	$380	$410		Q	EN

Breakfast: Cooked

Guest rooms:
Ambience:
Setting/location:

LOW   HIGH

Browns Boutique Hotel

Nigel and Bridget Brown
26 Isle Street, Queenstown
Tel: 03 4412050
Fax: 03 4412060
stay@brownshotel.co.nz
www.lodgings.co.nz – keyword: browns

Property features
Views over lake to Remarkables
Quiet location close to town centre
Central heating
Guest lounge with open fire
Courtyard/outdoor seating
Ski room
Local features
Skifields/outdoor pursuits
Restaurants/cafes - 5 min walk
Lake/water sports/jet boating
Gondola - 5 min walk

Queenstown - 3 mins walk
Wanaka - 1 hour drive

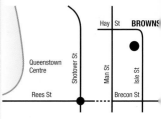

Entering Queenstown on SH
6A, continue on Stanley St to
roundabout. Turn left into Shotover
St, first right into Camp St and
second left into Isle St. Lodge is near
the top of the hill on the left.

Browns Boutique Hotel is, as its name suggests, a ten bedroom purpose-built accommodation, which is situated right in the heart of Queenstown. A three-minute walk down a lane brought me to the action part of town - the cafes, restaurant bars and boutique shops. The hotel building hints at a Mediterranean style in the white, rough-plastered walls of the spacious rooms and the glass doors that open to Juliet balconies, where guests get the full advantage of views of the Remarkable Mountains, Queenstown Hill and Lake Wakatipu. Each room is similar and thoughtfully equipped with everything you might need. The bathrooms in all rooms are fully tiled and the fittings and furnishings throughout are of a very high quality. Downstairs an attractively tiled and walled courtyard with outdoor furniture and a good view of the mountains is a great place to catch the sun. For colder weather there is a large lounge/library with an open fire and leather chairs with the ambience of an exclusive club. Breakfast which is either cooked or continental is served in the well-appointed dining room.

Accommodation available (NZ$)	👤	👤👤	+👤	🛏	🛁	Family dog on site
10 Rooms	$260-270	$280-290		K/T	EN	Breakfast: Cooked

Guest rooms:
Ambience:
Setting/location:

LOW   HIGH

Property features
Spectacular views
Central Queenstown - 4 min walk
15 guestrooms including suites
Local features
Walking tracks
Golf courses
Skifields
Vineyards/wineries
Rose gardens

Queenstown House
Louise Kiely
69 Hallenstein St, Queenstown
Tel: 03 4429043
Fax: 03 4428755
queenstown.house@xtra.co.nz
www.lodgings.co.nz – keyword: queenstownhouse

Queenstown central - 4 min walk
Dunedin - 3 hours drive

From Hwy 6, drive down hill to roundabout in central Queenstown, turn right into Ballarat St, left into Hallenstein St. The house is 50 metres on right on the corner of Malaghan St.

Queenstown House is an institution in this, the tourist capital of New Zealand. Not just because the central part of the hotel has been there for more than 25 years, it's more about the pivotal element in this, the bubbly, gracious hostess Louise Kiely who has recently celebrated 25 years as the hostess. So central, only four minutes walk from all the action of central Queenstown, the hotel offers a variety of accommodation from two bedroom villa suites with lounge, kitchen, a complete home way from home, to very comfortable ensuite rooms in the main house all tastefully decorated. All have either extensive lake or alpine views and there are numerous patio's and decks for just relaxing. Settle in and join Louise in the fireside sitting room or the lakeview deck for her legendary pre dinner drinks and complimentary nibbles including fine New Zealand cheeses. We found this was a great meeting place and a chance to chat to our fellow guests, share plans and Louise who has invaluable knowledge of all that is happening was happy to advise and set us in the right direction. Queenstown House does not have this prestigious name and reputation for nothing; it is a part of the culture of this town and it has been earned over many years through providing exceptional hosting to holiday makers and Louise has gained many life long friends.

Accommodation available (NZ$)	👤	👥	+👤	🛏	🛁
3 Rooms	$250	$295		Q	EN
8 Rooms	$250	$295		K or 2S	EN
2 Suites		$495-695	55	K	EN
1 S/C unit	$425	$495		K	EN

Breakfast: Special cooked
Evening meal: Enquire
Guest rooms:
Ambience:
Setting/location:

Evening meals by prior arrangement

LOW   HIGH

179

Remarkables Lodge

Colleen Ryan Brian Savage
595 Kingston Road, SH6, Queenstown
Tel: 03 4422720   Mob: 021619539
Fax: 03 4422730
contact@remarkables.co.nz
www.lodgings.co.nz – keyword: remarkables

qualmark
★ ★ ★ ★ ★
guest & hosted

(P) 🚶 ⊠ 📺 (C) ♿

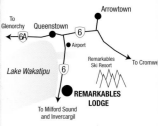

Property features
Cosy bar with snooker table
Spacious lounge with log fire
Swimming pool/sauna/spa pool
Tennis court/croquet
Helipad for heliskiing/fishing
Outside seating areas/fireplace
Local features
Remarkables ski field - 2 mins
3 golf courses - within 10 mins
Walking trails from Lodge
En route to Milford Sound

Queenstown - 10 mins drive
Arrowtown - 10 mins drive

To Glenorchy
Queenstown
6A
Arrowtown
6
Airport
Lake Wakatipu
6
Remarkables Ski Resort
To Cromwe
REMARKABLES LODGE
To Milford Sound and Invercargil

Follow SH6 (to Milford Sound/
Invercargill) at Frankton, passed the
airport and over the one-way bridge.
Continue passed the Remarkables
Ski resort and the lodge is on the lef

Nestled at the foothills of the Remarkables mountain range, this refurbished historic lodge is set on two acres of peaceful, landscaped gardens. It wasn't difficult to see why the original station owners chose this location for their home. This picturesque playground showcased gardens of fruit trees, deer in surrounding fields and a walk to a waterfall. Inside the lodge, a bar and games room, formal dinning area and a roaring log fire in the lounge in the winter are the height of luxury. I was invited to mingle around the pool table for pre-dinner drinks, although there was a temptation to sneak away to enjoy Colleen and Brian's impressive library of books. All seven bedrooms were ensuite with claw foot baths and suites have balconies. I was greeted in the morning by the sight of the stunning Remarkables towering into the sky virtually out of the back garden. Breakfast was a delight prepared by the resident chef, with homemade breads and pastries, bottled fruit from the garden and a choice from the cooked breakfast menu. A six-course dinner is also included in the tariff. Only a ten-minute drive from Queenstown's centre, Remarkables Lodge is and ideal place to stay in any season.

Accommodation available (NZ$)	👤	👤👤	+👤	🛏	🛁	Guest pets by arrangement
4 Suites	$950	$1275		SK+2S	EN	Breakfast: Special cooked
3 Rooms	$700	$990		SK or Q	EN	Evening meal: Included

Guest rooms:
Ambience:
Setting/location:

LOW   HIGH

Ski gear drying room available.

Property features
- Log construction/lake views
- Large open fireplace
- Rural setting/farm animals
- Laundry facilities
- Cot and highchair

Local features
- Guided fishing/walks/birdwatching
- Milford and Doubtful Sound
- Milford/Routeburn Tracks
- Hollyford/Kepler Tracks
- Golf course/kayaking

Fiordland Lodge & Log Cabins

Ron and Robynne Peacock
472 Te Anau - Milford Highway, Te Anau
Tel: 03 2497832
Fax: 03 2497449
info@fiordlandlodge.co.nz
www.lodgings.co.nz – keyword: fiordland

Te Anau - 5 mins drvie
Queenstown - 2 hrs drive

From Te Anau, drive north approximately 5km on SH 94 towards Milford Sound. Just past Sinclair Rd turn right into driveway signposted Fiordland Lodge. Continue to end of driveway.

Set among the breathtaking views of Lake Te Anau and Fiordland National Park, you will find elegant Fiordland Lodge. The architecture is one which keeps in tune with the splendour of its stunning surrounding landscape, with its striking natural timber construction, high ceilings, full trunk pillars and its inviting and massive river-stone fireplace. I was warmly welcomed by my hosts, who showed me to my room. All rooms and cabins have magnificent views and are exquisitely decorated to suit the most discerning traveller or business person. With its conference room (accommodating up to 25 persons) it is also the ideal venue for your corporate retreat. I couldn't help but relax in the bar where I enjoyed my complimentary pre dinner drinks and utilised the great gathering place to discuss and plan the following day's activities. Robynne and Ron are passionately involved in outdoor activities and will assist with all you're planning. There is so much to do in this amazing part of New Zealand: rivers to fish – more than 40, walks through alpine forests and guided bird watching. After all this we enjoyed top New Zealand cuisine served in the beautiful dining area, complimented by the superb wine from the cellar. The following days breakfast was just as wonderful and a great way to start an adventurous day – and what a day it was.

Family pets on site

Accommodation available (NZ$)	👤	👤👤	+👤	🛏	🛁
Breakfast: Special cooked					
Lodge Room	$340-680	$540-880		SK or 2S	EN
Evening meal: Table d'hote					
Exec Suite	$440-880	$640-1080		SK or 2S	EN
Guest rooms:					
1 S/C log cab	$240-440	$440-640	$200	Q+3S	PR
Ambience:					
1 S/C log cab	$240-440	$440-640	$200	Q+2S	PR
Setting/location:					

All rooms include dinner, bed and breakfast. Rates are subjet to seasonal changes.

The Ridge over Blueskin

Mike Turfus
603 Blueskin Road, Port Chalmers, Dunedin
Tel: 03 4822126   Mob: 0272224858
Fax: 03 4822125
relax@theridgeoverblueskin.co.nz
www.lodgings.co.nz – keyword: ridgeoverblueskin

Property features
Stunning views of Otago coastline
Total privacy in a peaceful setting
1900 settlers cottage
Romatic getaway/helipad
Special packages available
Local features
Dunedin City
Port Chalmers cafes & restaruants
Scenic helicopter flights
Orokonui Eco-Sanctuary
Royal albatross colony

Dunedin - 20 mins drive
Port Chalmers - 6 mins drive

THE RIDGE
OVER BLUESKIN

From Dunedin, travel North for 15
mins until you reach Waitati townsh[i]
Turn right at Blueskin Nurseries into
Harvey St. Travel 1km and veer righ[t]
into Mount Cargill Road, continue fo[r]
3.4kms. Turn left into Blueskin Rd,
the cottage is 3.9km along this roa[d]

Winding up the ridge out of Blueskin Bay, north of Dunedin, there's a Ridge Over Blueskin sign at the driveway. It's steep, lifting the visitor toward a high ridgeline under which nestles Mike and Michelle's lovely home. A little further along placed just out of site of the homestead, is a delight. A traditional southern worker's cottage. Many times otherwise faultless accommodation is found to suffer from the highways roar. Here, high on the ridge, well above Blueskin's little travelled road, there is only the sighing of trees, the rustle of mountain grass and the cry of wildlife. And those views! Is this what the eagle experiences looking down from his eyrie? Certainly this magical position evokes such feeling. Bathed in sun from dawn to dusk, the cottage has an old world charm. It emanates grace and tranquillity. Such romance, yet having every modern convenience for when the descending sun draws its soft mantle over the ocean. "It's proved popular for those very special occasions," confides Mike. "Anniversaries, honeymoons and time-out". Set in the Flagstaff conservation area, across the valley from the Orokonui Eco-sanctuary, Blueskin is attracting ecologically minded guest interest. Whether it's romance, time out or wildlife that leads one to Blueskin, it's an experience to treasure.

Accommodation available (NZ$)	♟	♟♟	+♟	🛏	🛁
1 Cottage	$330	$385		K	PR

Breakfast: Special cooked
Evening meal: $85-105pp
Guest rooms:
Ambience:
Setting/location:

LOW   HIG[H]

Property features
Historic mansion (1863)
Extensive gardens (8 acres)
City & harbour views
Licensed restaurant
Organic produce grown on site
Fr, Ger, Spa, Dutch & Rus spoken
Local features
Historic buildings/museums
Albatross colony/penguins
Taieri Gorge Railway/golf courses

Corstorphine House
Irina and Nico Francken
23A Milburn St, Corstorphine, Dunedin
Tel: 03 4871000
Fax: 03 4876672
info@corstorphine.co.nz
www.lodgings.co.nz – keyword: corstorphine

City centre - 10 mins drive
Oa maru - 1 hour drive

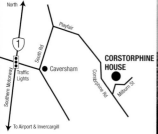

Take Caversham turnoff from SH 1,
just south of city centre. Turn into
South Rd. Turn right into Playfair St.
Continue to Corstorphine Rd then left
into Milburn St. Lodge is on your left.

When royalty travel, great care is exercised in the choice of accommodations. So much to consider. Security, of course. Refuge, perhaps. Tranquillity, very much so. Yet the location must not be remote. Above all facilities must exceed expectation. Irina and Nico's private hotel, Corstorphine House, fulfils all requirements of the most privileged of travellers. Yet Corstophine is available to any of us wishing, even for just a short while, to experience the ambience of this historic mansion. And what a grand experience! From the moment the security gate opens, one is in a world of privilege. Valet parking, bags whisked away. Some refreshment perhaps, before familiarisation of the house and 8 acres of lawn and garden. "We do everything we can on the premises" explains Irina. "Eggs come from our own hens. We bake our own bread, cakes and pastries." All the vegetables are organically grown on the property. "In fact we even make our own ice cream and chocolate." Irina adds with a laugh. How can one review a property where every detail, even down to choice of pillow, is anticipated? Where staff are so courteous, so accommodating? Where the hotel itself and its décor, sumptuous and faultless? One cannot. Corstorphine is above our terms of reference.

Accommodation available (NZ$)	👤	👥	+👤	🛏	🛁
6 Rooms	$380-725	$435-790	$65	K	EN
1 Room	$380-725	$435-790	$65	2Q	EN
1 Room	$380	$435	$65	Q+1S	PR

Breakfast: Special cooked
Evening meal: Menu
Guest rooms:
Ambience:
Setting/location:

LOW   HIGH

Season rates apply. Enquire for Dinner Bed and Breakfast or
Entire House POA.

Glenfield House

Lyndsey and Guy Farland
3 Peel Street, Mornington, Dunedin
Tel: 03 4535923   Mob: 021564615
Fax: 03 4535984
glenfieldhouse@xtra.co.nz
www.lodgings.co.nz – keyword: glenfieldhouse

Property features
Private dining on request
Adjacent to park
Sunny private garden
Guest kitchen
Local features
Art gallery/museum
Carisbrooke rugby stadium
Railway station
Speights brewery tour
Dunedin wildlife

Dunedin Central - 3 mins drive
Queenstown - 3 hour drive

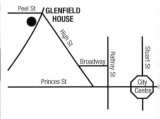

From the Octagon drive south towar
Princes St. At Casino right into
Rattray St. First left onto Broadway.
At lights right into High St. Peel St a
very top on the left.

Boutique Lodge accommodation offers one the opportunity to appreciate some of New Zealand's fine architecture. Dunedin's early wealth saw many noble homes magnificently crafted of beautiful native timbers. Sadly, most have gone, leaving Glenfield a treasure indeed. Built in 1884 the house epitomises the noble home of yesteryear, lovingly restored and maintained to a high standard by owners Lyndsey and Guy. Set above the city, there's a view to the port and over a tumble of well established homes, to the city. For the visitor, Glenfield's position is excellent. The Octagon, Dunedin city's hub, a brisk down hill walk offers a huge selection of restaurants, cafes and other attractions. It is a mix of this convenience, and the host's attention to their guest, that ensures Glenfield Houses patronage. This was demonstrated following an excellent evening meal at an Octagon restaurant Lyndsey recommended. "Glenfield House!" exclaimed the taxi driver. We've never known a taxi driver so attentive. It appears that for several years now, high court judges make Glenfield their home when presiding in Dunedin which speaks volumes for both house and hosts. "We involve ourselves as little or as much as our guests wish," says Lyndsey "and for those inclined, Barley the labrador is available to take guests for walks".

Accommodation available (NZ$)	👤	👤👤	+👤	🛏	🛁		
1 Suite	$350	$350		K	EN	Breakfast: Special cooked	
1 Room	$325	$325		K	EN	Evening meal: Enquire	
1 Room	$275	$275		Q	EN	Guest rooms:	
1 Room	$225	$225		Q	PR	Ambience:	
						Setting/location:	

Property features
Beautiful eco-retreat
Stunning water views
Eco-expeditions & massage available
Original local art
Separate to hosts dwelling
Retreat bookings available
Local features
Royal Albatross Colony
Beach and walking tracks
Wildlife viewing

Kaimata

Rachel Duell Kyle Davidson
297 Cape Saunders Road, Papanui Inlet,
Otago Peninsula
Tel: 03 4563443   Mob: 0210624053
Fax: 03 4563444
info@kaimatanz.com
www.lodgings.co.nz – keyword: kaimata

 8

Dunedin - 30 mins drive
Christchurch - 4 hrs 30 mins drive

From Dunedin follow Portsmouth
Drive to Portobello Village, right onto
Alans Beach Rd, continue straight
to Hoopers Inlet, left & continue until
Cape Saunders Rd signpost (2km), left
continue to Papanui Inlet. Right onto
Cape Saunders Rd & arrive at Kaimata.

This is special. This is so different. But within the limits this page imposes; let us endeavour to paint a picture of what delights await. An experience such as Kaimata must be sought out. It is not of the ordinary. It requires the traveller to leave well trodden highways for a less frequented road. And finally, for many of us city dwellers, the novelty of driving the typical, roading that serves New Zealand's remote farming community. Drive slowly. There is much to be seen before Kaimata's identifying sign. What reward awaits! One is torn between an orientation tour of the retreat itself and the extraordinary vista it affords. Built in contemporary style of local stone with huge beams of fragrant Macrocarpa, a timber, felled and milled on the property. Let's just sit and absorb for a while. Good heavens, what are those animals swimming in the bay below? Sea lions are only the start of wildlife discovery. Fur seals, native bush and wading bird, gull, penguin and albatross colonies, the area has it all. Photo opportunities are endless and local guides available. For the young and vigorous, there's a surf beach just over the hill. But maybe some time for quiet contemplation. Maybe we will be lucky enough to see the species interaction between a passing sea lion and cows grazing the shoreline grass. And we haven't even left the deck.

Accommodation available (NZ$)	👤	👤👤	+👤	🛏	🛁
1 Room		$310-350	$50	K+S	EN
1 Room		$280-320		Q	EN
1 Room		$265-295		Q	EN
S/C house		$640-850		K+2Q+S	EN/PR

Breakfast: Continental

Guest rooms:
Ambience:
Setting/location:

LOW   HIGH

Kaimata offers self-catering or hosted accomodation. For privacy & complete ambience book the retreat or guest share when you book a room.

Highland Peaks

Di and Peter Espie
333 Chain Hills Road, RD 1, Dunedin
Tel: 03 4896936   Mob: 0273510646
Fax: 03 4896924
info@highlandpeaks.com
www.lodgings.co.nz – keyword: highlandpeaks

Property features
Panoramic mountain/sea views
21 acres grounds
Newly completed
Eco-friendly design/guided ecotours
Hydrotherapy spa pool
Local features
Royal Albatross colony/rare penguins
Dunedin heritage architecture
Beachs/walks/rail & nature tours
Art galleries/botanic gardens
Fine dining/cafes/museums

Dunedin - 15 mins drive
Mosgiel - 7 mins drive

From SH1 take Mosgiel exit, turn towards Kinmont. Continue along Quarry Rd and Morris Rds over motorway. Turn left into Chain Hills Rd, take left fork to road end.

A short drive from Dunedin city and the airport, Highland Peaks feels as if it were in its own world. This new, eco-friendly lodge is sited on a ridge. Views are breathtaking. Constructed of natural stone and timbers, décor and layout is unashamedly 21st century. "We solar heat our water and the building is set to maximise natural sun". Peter knows about these things. He has a doctorate in ecology and is a former director of NZ's National Trust. His passion is conservation and the environment. It is his delight to lead wildlife tours, an option taken by many Highland Peaks guests as Otago is rich in wildlife conservation areas. From huge sea lions to tiny penguins Doctor Peter's explanations are an option not to be missed. Short of time? Explore the property's 21 acres of farm and forest walks. Friendly sheep will hope for a handful of hay! Finally there is a log fire, New Zealand wine and Di's cooking. "Good cuisine is important to us" she says, breakfast is a lavish affair and "no matter how full of activities, a fine dinner and a friendly glass makes a great end to the day".

Accommodation available (NZ$)	♂	♂♂	+♂	🛏	🛁	Family pets on site	
1 Suite	$195-255	$250-350		K	EN		
1 Suite	$195-255	$245-295		SK or 2S	PR		
1 Suite	$325-375	$350-450		SK or 2S	EN		

Gym equipment, CD & DVD library, BBQ, mountain bikes, personal guided nature tours available.

Breakfast: Special cooked
Evening meal: $40-100pp
Guest rooms:
Ambience:
Setting/location:

LOW   HIGH

Property features
Restored NZ Settler's Mansion
Llifestyle block property
Aromatheraby baths/sauna/massage
Guest library/books/DVD's
Pentanque/croquet/board games
Local features
Fishing/hunting/skiing/golf
World Renowned Mataura River
Private access to Pomahaka River
West Otago's Blue Mountains
Walks/wilderness dining

Mainholm Country Lodge

Graham and Sandi Larsen
592 Pomahaka Road, Conical Hills, West Otago
Tel: 03 2048024
Fax: 03 2048080
info@mainholmlodge.co.nz
www.lodgings.co.nz – keyword: mainholm

Tapanui - 8 mins drive
Invercargill - 1 hr 13 mins drive

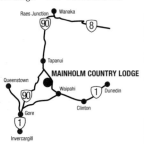

From Gore head north on Hwy 1 for 5.5km. Turn left onto Hwy 90 towards Tapanui and travel 26Km. Turn right into Pomahaka Rd (Waipahi). Contine 6.1km along Pomahaka Rd to Mainholm

　　　Mainholm Lodge a true example of early New Zealand architecture is situated in the heart of West Otago. With all the early Victorian grandeur of yesteryear the lodge offers all the comforts to make your stay warm and relaxing. Hosts Graham and Sandi have lovingly restored this fine home, which offers four guest rooms, each decorated with the finest antiques and linens and beautiful views of the surrounding mountains and country side. There is no shortage of comforts here and each bedroom has a TV, DVD, and fireplace. Graham and Sandy delight in spoiling their guests, join them for pre dinner drinks in the house bar. Dinner, prepared using the freshest of ingredients is a highlight and served in one of three romantic dining rooms. Their restaurant is also open to the public and caters for every occasion. The West Otago region boosts beautiful scenery and a relaxed way of life. There is also an abundance of local activities including fishing in the Pomahaka River, well known for brown trout, and golf at the local course in Tapanui, Ski fields and lakes are but a few hours away, as are a whole host of wineries. This is also a perfect base for exploring the beauty of the Catlins. Mainholm Lodge offers wonderful Southern Hospitality and a truly memorable experience.

Family cat on site Guest pets by arrangement	Accommodation available (NZ$)	👤	👤👤	+👤	🛏	🛁
Breakfast: Special continental	1 Room	$195	$235		Q	EN
Evening meal: Available	1 Room	$175	$215		Q	EN
Guest rooms:	1 Room	$125	$165	$45	Q + S	PR
Ambience:	1 Room	$125	$165		D	PR
Setting/location:	Meeting room caters for up to 20 people. Cooked breakfast additional $7-10pp					

LOW　　　HIGH

187

Sails Ashore

Iris and Peter Tait
11 View Street, Stewart Island
Tel: 032191151
Free: 08007839278
tait@sailsashore.co.nz
www.lodgings.co.nz – keyword: sailsashore

Property features
Central but private location
Superb views of harbour & village
Set in native exotic garden
Local features
In house guided Ulva Island
Scenic road tours
Charter yacht/day cruises
Fishing trips/museum & DoC
Local day walks & attractions
Kiwi encounters/kayaking/diving

Halfmoon Bay - 4 mins walk
Invercargill - 20 mins flight

Sails Ashore is situated within the central village of Stewart Island, overlooking Halfmoon Bay and only 5 minutes stroll from the waterfront. You can either catch a ferry from Bluff or take a flight to Stewart Island

The Southern most member of Boutique Lodgings, Sails Ashore is located on remote Stewart Island which although remote is very easy to get to and you will be rewarded, for this is a very special place. The journey to Sails Ashore is an adventure, either by ferry or plane or to spice up life a little, helicopter. Our hosts Peter and Iris have been here many years with Peter arriving in 1969 as the Forest Service Ranger, a position that has grown to become the Department of Conservation. Sails Ashore situated over spectacular Half Moon Bay has two king suites tastefully decorated using recycled and salvaged Rimu with all amenities to make our stay perfect. The balcony was a great place to sit with a drink and enjoy the view but not for too long. The opportunity to visit the renowned Ulva Island was a draw card. Peter offers guided tours for up to six people to this unique haven for bird life, fauna and flowers that are in many cases not found anywhere else. Peter and Iris's knowledge is unsurpassed and this is a must do activity. A hearty breakfast set us up for the following day as we walked the islands roads and chatted with the locals. Time is no issue here – fish and chips by the shore, a beer in the local hotel. Peter and Iris are superb hosts and their commitment to sustainable tourism is something to be admired.

Accommodation available (NZ$)	👤	👤👤	+👤	🛏	🛁	Family pets on site
2 Rooms	$380	$380		K	ES	Breakfast: Special continental

Index

For your convenience we have alphabetically listed the place names of centres or areas where we have properties. Appropriate page numbers are then listed for property reference.